THE
LYLE
ANTIQUES
& THEIR VALUES

CLOCKS
& WATCHES

Identification & Price Guide

COMPILED & EDITED BY
TONY CURTIS

The publishers wish to express their sincere thanks to the following for their involvement and assistance in the production of this volume:—

KAREN DOUGLASS
JANICE MONCRIEFF
ANNETTE CURTIS
TANYA FAIRBAIRN
SALLY DALGLIESH
FRANK BURRELL
ROBERT NISBET
LOUISE SIMPSON
JONN DUNLOP
EILEEN BURRELL

Printed in Denmark by ⊞ Nørhaven A/S, Viborg
ISBN 0-86248-104-X

INTRODUCTION

While this series of handy volumes has been specially devised to provide busy dealers and collectors with an extremely comprehensive reference library of antiques and their values, the information will also prove to be of great general interest to those with just a few pieces they wish to sell or appraise.

Each volume is crammed with over 2,000 detailed illustrations highlighting the distinguishing features of a broadly representative selection of specialised antiques and collectibles accompanied by descriptions and prices computed from recent auction figures.

We have endeavoured to obtain a balance between the more expensive collector's items and those which, although not in their true sense antiques, are handled daily by the antiques trade.

The illustrations and prices in the following sections have been arranged to make it easy for the reader to assess the period and value of all items with speed.

When dealing with the more popular trade pieces, in some instances a calculation of an average price has been estimated from the varying accounts researched.

As regards prices, when 'one of a pair' is given in the description the price quoted is for a pair and so that we can make maximum use of the available space it is generally considered that one illustration is sufficient. This will also apply when a description reads eg; part of a service, suite or a set.

It will be noted that in some descriptions taken directly from sales catalogues originating from many different countries, some terms are used in a broader sense than is customary, but in all cases the term used is self explanatory.

Pocket size with a sturdy binding, perfect for use in shops, flea markets and at auctions, *The Lyle Antiques and Their Values Identification and Price Guides* are your keys to smart antique buying or selling.

Tony Curtis

ACKNOWLEDGEMENTS

Abridge Auctions, (Michael Yewman) Market Place, Abridge, Essex RM4 1UA
Anderson & Garland, Anderson House, Market Street, Newcastle. NE1 6XA
Banks & Silvers, 66 Foregate Street, Worcester.
Barbers Fine Art Auctioneers, The Mayford Centre, Smarts Heath Road, Mayford, Woking.
Bearnes, Rainbow, Avenue Road, Torquay. TQ2 5TG
Biddle & Webb, Ladywood, Middleway, Birmingham. B16 0PP
Bloomsbury Book Auctions, 3 & 4 Hardwick Street, London.
Boardman Fine Art Auctioneers, Station Road Corner, Haverhill, Suffolk. CB9 0EY
Bonhams, Montpelier Galleries, Montpelier Street, Knightsbridge, London. SW7 1HH
Bracketts, 27-29 High Street, Tunbridge Wells, Kent. TN1 1UU
J. R. Bridgford & Sons, 1 Heyes Lane, Alderley Edge, Cheshire.
British Antique Exporters, 206 London Road, Burgess Hill, W. Sussex. RH15 9RX
Brogden & Co., 38 & 39 Silver Street, Lincoln.
Wm. H. Brown, Westgate Hall, Grantham, Lincs. NG31 6LT
Lawrence Butler & Co., Butler House, 86 High Street, Hythe, Kent. CT21 5AJ
Capes, Dunn & Co., The Auction Galleries, 38 Charles Street, Manchester. M1 7DB
Chancellors Hollingsworth, 31 High Street, Ascot, Berkshire. SL5 7HG
Christie's, 8 King Street, St. James's, London. SW1Y 6QT
Christie's, 502 Park Avenue, New York, N. Y. 10022
Christie's, Cornelis Schuystraat 57, 1071 JG, Amsterdam, Holland.
Christie's East, 219 East 67th Street, New York, N. Y. 10021
Christie's & Edminston's, 164-166 Bath Street, Glasgow.
Christie's S. Kensington Ltd., 85 Old Brompton Road, London. SW7 3LD
Coles, Knapp & Kennedy, Georgian Rooms, Ross-on-Wye, Herefordshire. HR9 5HL
Cooper Hirst, Goldway House, Parkway, Chelmsford. CM20 7PR
Dacre, Son & Hartley, 1-5 The Grove, Ilkley, Yorkshire.
Dee & Atkinson, The Exchange Saleroom, Driffield, N. Humberside. YO25 7LJ
Dickson, Davy & Markham, Elwes Street, Brigg, S. Humberside. DN20 8LB
Wm. Doyle Galleries Inc., 175 East 87th Street, New York.
Dreweatts, Donnington Priory, Donnington, Newbury, Berkshire.
Hy. Duke & Son, Fine Art Salerooms, Weymouth Avenue, Dorchester, Dorset. DT1 1DG
Elliott & Green, Auction Salerooms, Emsworth Road, Lymington, Hants, SO4 9ZE
R. H. Ellis & Sons, 44-46 High Street, Worthing, West Sussex. BN11 1LL
Farrant & Wightman, 2/3 Newport Street, Old Town, Swindon.
John D. Fleming & Co., 8 Fore Street, Dulverton, Somerset. TA22 9EX
Fox & Sons, 5 & 7 Salisbury Street, Fordinbridge, Hants. SP6 1AD
Geering & Colyer, 22-26 High Street, Tunbridge Wells. TN1 1XA
Rowland Gorringe, 15 North Street, Lewes, Sussex.
Goss & Crested China Ltd., N. J. Pine, 62 Murray Road, Horndean, Hants. PO8 9JL
Andrew Grant, 59-60 Foregate Street, Worcester.
Graves, Son & Pilcher, 71 Church Road, East Sussex. BN3 2GL
Giles Haywood, The Auction House, St. John's Road, Stourbridge, W. Midlands. DY8 1EW
Heathcote Ball & Co., The Old Rectory, Appleby Magna, Leicestershire.
Hobbs & Chambers, 'At the Sign of the Bell', Market Place, Cirencester, Gloucestershire. GL7 1QQ
Honiton Galleries, High Street, Honiton, Devon.
Edgar Horn, 46-50 South Street, Eastbourne, Sussex. BN21 4XB
Jacobs & Hunt, Lavant Street, Petersfield, Hampshire. GU32 3EF
W. H. Lane & Son, 64 Morrab Road, Penzance, Cornwall. TR18 2QT
Lawrence Fine Art, South Street, Crewkerne, Somerset. TA18 8AB
James & Lister Lea, 11 Newhall Street, Birmingham.
Locke & England, 18 Guy Street, Leamington Spa, Warwickshire. CV32 4DG
Thomas Love & Son, South St. John Street, Perth, Scotland.
R. J. Lucibell, 7 Fontayne Avenue, Rainham, Essex.
Mallams, 24 St. Michael's Street, Oxford.
May, Whetter & Grose, Cornubia Hall, Par, Cornwall.
Moore, Allen & Innocent, 33 Castle Street, Cirencester, Gloucestershire. GL7 1QD
Morphets, 4-6 Albert Street, Harrogate, Yorkshire. HG1 1JL
Neales of Nottingham, 192 Mansfield Road, Nottingham. NG1 3HX
D. M. Nesbit & Co., 7 Clarendon Road, Southsea, Hants. PO5 2ED
Onslows Auctioneers, 14-16 Carroun Road, London. SW8 1JT
Osmond, Tricks, Regent Street Auction Rooms, Clifton, Bristol, Avon. BS8 4HG
Outhwaite & Litherland, Kingsway Galleries, Fontenoy Street, Liverpool. L3 2BE
Phillips, The Old House, Station Road, Knowle, Solihull, W. Midlands. B93 0HT
Phillips Auctioneers, The Auction Rooms, 1 Old King Street, Bath, Avon. BA1 1DD
John H. Raby & Son, 21 St. Mary's Road, Bradford.
Reeds Rains, Trinity House, 114 Northenden Road, Sale, Manchester. M33 3HD
Russell, Baldwin & Bright, Ryelands Road, Leominster, Herefordshire. HR6 8JG
Sandoe, Luce Panes, Wotton Auction, Rooms, Wotton-under-Edge, Gloucestershire. GL12 7EB
Robert W. Skinner Inc., Bolton Gallery, Route 117, Bolton, Massachusetts.
H. Spencer & Sons Ltd., 20 The Square, Retford, Notts.
Stalker & Boos, 280 North Woodward Avenue, Birmingham, Michigan.
David Stanley Auctions, Stordan Grange, Osgathorpe, Leics. LE12 9SR
Street Jewellery Society, 10 Summerhill Terrace, Newcastle-upon-Tyne.
Stride & Son, Southdown House, St. John's Street, Chichester, Sussex.
G. E. Sworder & Sons, Chequers, 19 North Street, Bishops Stortford, Herts.
Theriault, P. O. Box 151 Annapolis, Maryland 21404.
Vidler & Co., Auction Offices, Cinque Ports At., Rye, Sussex.
Wallis & Wallis, West Street Auction Galleries, Lewes, Sussex. BN7 2NJ
Ward & Partners, 16 High Street, Hythe, Kent.
Warner, Wm. H, Brown, 16-18 Halford Street, Leicester. LE1 1JB
Warren & Wignall, 113 Towngate, Leyland, Lancashire.
Peter Wilson Fine Art Auctioneers, Victoria Gallery, Market Street, Nantwich. CW5 3DG
Wooley & Wallis, The Castle Auction Mart, Castle Street, Salisbury, Wiltshire. SP1 3SU
Eldon E. Worrall & Co., 15 Seel Street, Liverpool.
Worsfolds Auction Galleries, 40 Station Road West, Canterbury, Kent.

CONTENTS

CLOCKS & WATCHES

Over the past ten years there has been a great upsurge of interest among collectors for horological items.

The word 'horological' is carefully chosen because the field of clocks and watches is a minefield of strange expressions and terms for anyone entering into it for the first time.

As a simple guide it is best to know first of all that a *clock* is any timekeeper not designed to be carried in the pocket or worn. A *timepiece* however is a clock that strikes the hours every hour. A *regulator* is a clock, generally a timepiece, designed for precision timekeeping.

Going down the scale of size, a *watch* is a timekeeper with a balance that is designed to be carried in the pocket or worn, while a *clockwatch* is one that strikes the hours regularly.

A Louis XVI ormolu cartel clock, the enamel dial signed Brille a Paris, 14in. high. (Christie's) £4,400

An English lantern clock, dial signed Nicholas Coxeter, 14½in. high. (Christie's) £3,850

In the field of clocks on their own, a new crop of terms is encountered. A *lantern clock* dates from between 1600 and 1750 and is usually a metal cased, weight driven wall clock though there are some spring driven later varieties.

A *cartel clock* is a decorative spring driven wall clock, often French, from the 18th century or later.

The means by which these clocks keep time is also a source of particular names. The *mystery* or *mysterieuse is a timekeeper in which the means of maintaining the motion are not obvious; an automaton is one where* animated figures are actuated by the clock's movement.

Clocks that chime are always very popular and there is a large variety in the ways that this is done – *quarter striking clocks* sound every fifteen minutes on two to three bells or gongs but *chiming clocks*, while they sound every fifteen minutes as well, do so on four or more bells or gongs. *Petite sonnerie means that the clock sounds every quarter except on the hour but grande sonnerie infers that at the hour, the quarter is also sounded.*

Musical clocks are what they sound like and they play tunes on bells, gongs, pipes or steel combs and there are some clocks known as *repeaters, quarter repeaters* or *minute repeaters* which repeat the hours; the hours and quarters and the hours, quarters and minutes within each quarter respectively.

7

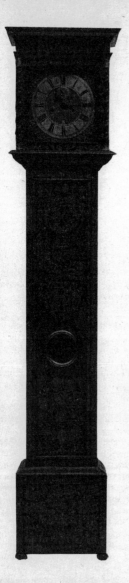

A Queen Anne kingwood striking bracket clock, the dial signed Cha. Gretton, 14in. high. (Christie's) £17,600

A brass chiming skeleton clock, on oval oak base with glass dome, English, circa 1900, 24in. high including dome. (Christie's) £3,837

In the world of watches, terms are equally esoteric. A *chronograph* is a stopwatch with a second hand that can be started, stopped and returned to zero at will. A *chronometer*, on the other hand, is a precision watch with a detent. escapement and is used on Continental watches tested to a certain degree of precision. So what is a *detent escapement?* It is a precision escapement invented in the 18th century and used in making marine and pocket chronometers.

Oignon is the term given to a large, bulbous French watch of the 17th and 18th centuries whereas, during that period English watch makers tended to prefer *pair cased watches* in which there were two cases for each watch — the inner case which

A fine William and Mary walnut and floral marquetry longcase clock by Christopher Gould, London. (Phillips) £19,500

A very rare silver tourbillion carriage clock with grande sonnerie striking and perpetual calendar by Charles Frodsham, London, hallmarked London 1918. (Phillips) £85,000

contained the movement could be removed from the outer for winding. This style was almost universal in English watches from 1650 to around 1800 but much less common in French watches.

A *hunting cased watch* had a front and back cover while *half hunters* were watches with small apertures in the front cover which showed the hands and dial. An *open faced watch* had no cover over the glass.

In more modern watches the terms *multi-calibrated chronograph* or *perpetual chronograph* are used to signify more than one calibrated scale in the first instance and a watch which has both perpetual calendar and chronograph work in the second. The *calibrated scale* is the graduated measurement found in a chronograph and a *register* is a subsidiary dial which records lapsed time.

Today with the advent of quartz watches and digital clocks there is no longer such necessity for every household to have its treasured timepiece, but as the family clock loses its pride of place in the middle of the mantelpiece, collectors are beginning to appreciate the artistry and craftsmanship that went into the making of them and are starting to seek out special, decorative examples.

Collecting clocks and watches is a field that will yield a good profit in years to come but it is important to learn as much as possible about this very complicated subject.

The most bouyant areas at the moment are wrist watches and long case clocks.

Until recently, watches had for some time been a fairly stagnant area partly because few good examples were coming onto the market but, in 1986, Sotheby's held a specialist sale of 400 wristwatches in New York when the Attwood collection was being thinned down and some spectacular prices were recorded. These prices gave an added stimulus to the market. They included a Swiss coaching watch which sold for £16,930 and an astronomical watch by Johan Sayller which made £16,369. Watches by English makers like Arnold, Earnshaw, Barwise and Frodsham also did well.

It is interesting that men's watches fetch far more money than women's and watches with special features like repeaters and alarms always do well. The world record for a wrist watch was set up when Christie's in Geneva sold a Patek Phillippe perpetual calendar bracelet watch with split second chronography for £102,500 in 1986. It had been made in Geneva only 31 years before.

At the moment, there is great interest among collectors for 19th century Swiss

A fine statuesque late 19th century rosewood crossbanded and marquetry inlaid musical long-case clock, 274cm. high. (Phillips) £5,000

precision watches by makers like Leroy and Fils; Breguet and Potter but high prices are also paid for more modern watches like Rolex — one of their Oyster Perpetual watches can make nearly £5,000 — and Vacheron and Constantin, which can sell for around £3,000. In fact any watch of quality and in good condition will fetch a reasonable price at auction.

This is also a good time to pick up bargains in mantel clocks and the prices in certain sectors have been rising steadily over the past few years. A case in point are black

A 19th century gold minute repeating grande sonnerie clockwatch with perpetual calendar, signed for Breguet. (Phillips) £23,000

A silvered bronze Art Deco table clock, signed R. Terras, 34,5cm. high. (Christie's) £990

marble – actually Belgian slate – clocks that used to decorate Victorian and Edwardian drawing rooms. Ten years ago they cost around £5, and were so common that one man bought them to use their slate bases for building his garden wall! Today the price is likely to be nearer £50. Spelter clocks were produced around the turn of the century by German and American manufacturers to meet the demand of the affluent middle classes and today they sell for between £100 and £200. At a higher price bracket, then as now, are Regency and Victorian bracket clocks which can cost anything up to £5,000. Ormolu and bronze Empire clocks can make around £1,000 – or more if they are decorated with Sevres panels which many of them were.

An Arts & Crafts square oak mantel clock, by Seth Thomas Clock Co., 20th century, 12½in. high, 10½in. wide. (Robt. W. Skinner Inc.) £648

A silvered bronze mantel clock, by Edgar Brandt, 30.6cm. high. (Christie's) £3,080

Ormolu clocks alone however, some of which were very rococo in style, have dropped in price over the past couple of years because of diminished interest from Middle Eastern buyers who used to snap them up.

An interesting development in the horological scene is the re-emergence into favour of the longcase clock. After peaking into four figures for even the most mundane examples around fifteen years ago, these clocks then saw a downturn in their prices. Now, however, interest in longcase clocks is re-kindling and a 17th century clock in walnut and panel marquetry signed by Bird of London recently sold for £11,500 at

A William III quarter repeating ebony bracket clock, signed Claudius Du Chesne, Londini Fecit, 16½in. high. (Christie's) £10,475

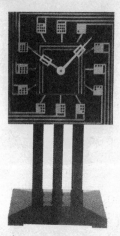

The Sturrock Domino clock, designed by Charles Rennie Mackintosh as a wedding present to Alec Sturrock and Mary Newbery, 25cm. high. (Phillips) £42,000

A good late 17th century architectural long-case clock by Joseph Knibb, London. (Phillips) £42,000

Phillips in Edinburgh while the same auction house found a bid of £42,000 for a Charles II longcase pearwood clock by Joseph Knibb of London.

Good Georgian clocks are also selling well at prices between £1,500 and £4,000 but the price for longcase clocks very much depends on the wood with which they are made — oak is usually fairly cheap unless the clock has a brass face. A pine clock is cheapest of all — at around £350 — but clocks in figured walnut and, best of all, mahogany, fetch top prices. A good 19th century grandmother clock in mahogany will fetch around £3,000.

Clocks from the Art Nouveau period are currently doing very well at auction, especially if the cases are decorated with characteristically flowing designs. Recently a longcase clock by J. Gruber made £2,500 because of its attractive Art Nouveau case. But of course the king of clocks, from recent times at least, must be Charles Rennie Macintosh's black and cream Domino Clock which he designed as a wedding present for an Edinburgh artist couple and which, when it came up for auction at Phillips last year sold for £42,000.

ACT OF PARLIAMENT CLOCKS

An 18th century Act of Parliament wall clock by J. Vulliamy of London, 4ft.1in. high, circa 1750.   £3,500

Black japanned and gilt decorated 'Act of Parliament' tavern clock by John Wilson, Peterborough.   £2,250

George III black-painted Act of Parliament wall timepiece, dial signed Henry Riddle, London, 5ft.2in. high.   £1,500

A lacquered tavern timepiece, with 25in. cream painted wooden dial, the case inscribed J. Bartholomew, 57in. high.   £3,300

A mahogany Act of Parliament clock, the 22in. dial signed Thos. De La Salle, London. £2,500

An 18th century striking Act of Parliament clock, signed Ino. Wilson, Peterborough, 56½in. high.   £990

A mid Georgian black japanned tavern or Act of Parliament clock signed Robert Allam, London, on the shaped 30in. dial, 59in. high.   £4,104

An Act of Parliament timepiece, signed beneath the dial Thomas Fenton, London.   £715

A George III black lacquered and chinoiserie decorated tavern wall timepiece, signed Frans. Perigal, London, 1.44m. high.   £900

ADVERTISING CLOCKS

Late 19th century moulded iron and zinc jeweller's trade sign, America. £405

A desk clock from Watts Tyre & Rubber Co. of Gloucestershire, in working order. £15

The Spalding Co. Iron Advertising trade sign, the cast-iron pocket watch frame with zinc painted face, 22¼in. high, circa 1890. £275

Shavallo battery advertising clock 'Saves Time'. £10

Jolly Tar wall timepiece, manufactured by Baird Clock Co., New York, 30½in. high. £890

Boston Beer Co. wall timepiece, manufactured by the New Haven Clock Co., circa 1900, 14in. diam. £430

Late 19th century 'Coca-Cola' walnut regulator timepiece, by Gilbert Clock Co., 30in. long. £250

Late 19th century Clock Shop trade sign, iron and zinc painted, 23in. wide. £135

Late 19th century pressed wood advertising timepiece, by Baird Adv. Clock Co., 31in. long. £1,085

AUTOMATON CLOCKS

An automaton clock in the form of a ship's bridge, 12½in. high.   £1,980

Late 18th century gilt metal musical automaton clock for the Oriental market, 19¾in. high.   £15,120

An automaton clock in the form of a waterwheel in brickwork surround, 16in. high.   £4,400

A 19th century mechanical organ automaton with clock, 26in. high.   £9,210

Mid 19th century Swiss musical automaton of singing birds, on oval base, 60cm. high.   £1,381

A Regency gilt bronze automaton mantel clock, the case in the form of a bird cage, signed Borrell, London, 1ft.7in. high.   £5,500

A three-dimensional wood model picture clock showing a French Chateau, under glass dome, 21½in. high.   £1,200

A mid 17th century South German negro automaton clock, 11½in. high.   £3,888

A Swiss automaton mantel clock, 9in. high.   £1,728

BANJO CLOCKS

Custom mahogany
weight driven banjo
timepiece with eagle
finial.   £850

American 19th century
banjo wall clock, 29in.
high.   £800

A Federal mahogany and
giltwood presentation banjo
timepiece, Mass., circa 1820,
40in. high.   £1,232

A Federal presentation
mahogany banjo time-
piece, by A. Willard,
circa 1820, 40½in. high.
          £1,680

The Col. Isaac Gardiner Reed
Presentation banjo clock, by
Aaron Willard, 1812-16,
35½in. high, including eagle.
          £84,675

A Federal mahogany and
eglomise banjo clock, by
Warren, Mass., 1815/30,
30in. high.   £2,124

A Federal giltwood banjo
timepiece with painted dial
and eight-day weight driven
movement, circa 1820, 41in.
high.   £845

American rosewood
banjo timepiece, circa
1870, 29in. long. £670

Federal giltwood mahogany
banjo timepiece, by Lemuel
Curtis, Mass., circa 1820,
32in. high.   £3,993

BANJO CLOCKS

Presentation banjo time-
piece, by Waltham Clock
Co., Mass., circa 1910,
37½in. high.   £735

Federal mahogany and
gilt stencilled banjo timepiece by Joshua Wilder,
circa 1820, 34in. high
£1,500

Late 19th century Water-
bury banjo type wall
clock with white porce-
lain face, 42in. high.
£750

Mid 19th century banjo timepiece with alarm, signed A.
Willard, Jnr., Boston, 33½in.
high.   £7,675

Early 19th century Federal
mahogany giltwood and
eglomise banjo clock, 33½in.
long.   £1,064

An early 19th century American mahogany cased wall
clock, 30in. high.   £550

A Federal mahogany gilt-
wood and eglomise banjo
clock, by Aaron Willard,
1820/25, 33¾in. high.
£1,972

A Federal mahogany and giltwood presentation banjo
timepiece, Mass., 37in. long.
£1,250

A Federal mahogany gilt-
wood and eglomise banjo
clock, Mass., 1815-25,
40in. high.   £950

BRACKET CLOCKS

An olivewood bracket clock, the 8in. dial signed Joseph Knibb, 14½in. high. £24,200

An 18th century Italian quarter-striking bracket clock, 25in. high. £1,226

19th century English mahogany and walnut crossbanded bracket clock with a silver dial and ormolu mounts. £400

A late Stuart tortoiseshell veneered case for a miniature bracket clock, 10in. high. £990

Late 18th century George III gilt and cut glass mounted floral painted quarter-chiming musical bracket clock for the Turkish market, signed Benj. Barber, London, 37½in. high. £32,271

A large astronomical calendar clock, the corner of the 15½in. dial with a plaque signed John Naylor, 38in. high. £42,900

A large bracket clock with eight-day Continental movement chiming on eight gongs, 27in. high. £400

A George III bracket clock with enamel dial, by Robt. Henderson, 15½in. high. £7,000

Late 18th century Austrian petite sonnerie bracket clock with carrying handle, 18½in. high. £455

BRACKET CLOCKS

A Victorian director's bracket clock with 8-day fusee movement chiming on eight bells, 30in. high. £1,500

An early 19th century bracket clock by Barwise, London, 13¼in. high. £1,450

An Austrian fruitwood quarter striking bracket clock, signed B. Schmidt, 20in. high. £935

An early George III padouk-wood automaton organ clock, by Wm. Vale, London, 37in. high. £8,800

A George III satinwood 'balloon' bracket clock, the enamel dial signed Webster London, 24in. high. £4,320

A Chinese carved hardwood bracket clock on stand, the movement with twin chain fusees, 22½in. high. £972

A Queen Anne kingwood striking bracket clock, the dial signed Cha. Gretton, 14in. high. £17,600

A chiming and repeating dome top bracket clock, nine bells and one gong, 19½in. high. £1,100

An early George III 8-day bracket clock with verge striking movement by Wm. Allam, 15.5in. high. £8,200

BRACKET CLOCKS
BOULLE

Mid 19th century ormolu mounted bracket clock, France, backplate engraved 'Fiault Paris, Reparee par Bourdin', 45in. high. £1,382

An ormolu mounted scarlet boulle bracket clock, dial signed V. Courtecuisse & Cie Lille, 45in. high. £1,870

A Regency boulle bracket clock, the dial signed Paliand a Besancon, 39½in. high. £1,296

A Regency boulle bracket clock, the dial signed Balthazar a Paris, with later movement, 39½in. high. £1,620

A large boulle bracket clock and pedestal, inlaid with cut brass on a tortoiseshell ground, 92in. high. overall. £2,550

A French gilt brass mounted boulle bracket clock, signed Leroy a Paris, 18in. high, excluding bracket. £858

French ormolu mounted boulle bracket clock in Louis XV style, with strike. £775

Early 19th century boulle timepiece, the movement signed Barraud & Lunds, 10½in. high. £640

An ebonised wood and gilt bronze bracket clock by Winterhalder & Hoffmeir, 27¼in. high, circa 1880. £400

BRACKET CLOCKS
BOULLE

Early 18th century bracket clock in red and green boulle case, the backplate engraved Jerome Martinot, Paris, 37in. high. £900

A 19th century tortoiseshell and cut brass inlaid bracket clock, signed Lepeltier a Paris, 2ft.2½in. high. £950

An ormolu mounted boulle bracket clock, the chapter ring signed J. Gudin a Paris, 41½in. high. £1,760

A contre-partie polychrome boulle bracket clock, the enamel face signed Gille L'Aine a Paris, basically 18th century, 31in. high. £1,650

An ormolu mounted boulle mantel clock, the enamel dial signed Grohe Paris, 11½in. high. £495

A Louis XIV French ormolu mounted boulle bracket clock, signed Gribelin a Paris, 49½in. high. £2,200

A Regence ormolu mounted boulle bracket clock, dial signed Mynuel a Paris, 32in. high. £1,540

A Louis XV style red boulle bracket clock with two-train movement by Gay Vicarino & Co., Paris, 44cm. high. £420

An ormolu mounted scarlet boulle bracket clock, the glazed dial with Roman enamel numerals, 48in. high. £2,420

BRACKET CLOCKS
EBONISED

Late 18th century ebonised and gilt brass decorated bracket clock, by Hayley & Milner, London. £1,100

Late Stuart ebonised striking bracket clock by John Barnett, London, 14½in. high. £2,250

An Austrian ebonised striking bracket clock with calendar and alarm, 19in. high. £800

An ebonised quarter chiming bracket clock, signed on an inset plaque Danl. Catlin, Lynn, 20in. high. £880

Mid 19th century George II ebony quarter-repeating bracket clock, signed Rich'd. Gregg, London, 13in. high. £3,227

A small ebony veneered bracket clock, signed John Drew Londini Fecit, 14½in. high. £1,980

A Charles II ebonised striking bracket clock, the square dial signed Hen. Jones London, 16in. high. £3,240

Mid 18th century George II ebonised quarter-chiming bracket clock, signed B. Gray, London, 15½in. high. £5,042

An ebonised gilt brass mounted quarter chiming bracket clock, signed Lambert & Co., London, 16½in. high. £1,210

BRACKET CLOCKS
EBONISED

An ebonised double basket top bracket clock with 7in. brass dial, 18¼in. high. £2,500

A 17th century bracket clock by Joseph Windmills, in an ebonised case, London, circa 1695. £14,000

A George III bracket clock in ebonised gilt mounted case, 20in. high overall. £720

A small and very fine veneered ebony quarter repeating bracket clock, the 6in. dial signed Tho. Tompion Londini fecit, 12½in. high. £40,000

A George III ebonised bracket clock, signed Eardley Norton, London, 19½in. high. £1,518

A Queen Anne ebony striking and quarter repeating bracket clock, signed Sam. Aldworth, 14in. high. £4,950

A George II ebonised quarter striking bracket clock, the dial signed Jams. Snelling, London, 14¾in. high. £3,080

A Charles II ebonised striking bracket clock, dial signed J. Windmills, London, 14¼in. high. ʼ£4,950

A James II ebonised Roman striking bracket clock of Phase III Type, signed Joseph Knibb, 12in. high. £11,880

BRACKET CLOCKS EBONISED

An ebony veneered quarter-repeating bracket clock, the 7½in. dial signed Windmills London, 18½in. high. £2,000

An ebonised bracket clock, dial signed Jonathan Lowndes, circa 1685, 13in. high. £2,250

A George II ebonised striking bracket clock, signed Wm. Webster, London, 17in. high. £5,000

A 19th century ebonised and brass mounted bracket clock, the silvered dial signed Payne, 163 New Bond St., London, 1ft.2½in. high. £1,000

An ebonised quarter-repeating bracket clock, the backplate signed Nathaniel Hodges, 12½in. high. £5,720

An ebonised wood bracket clock, by J. Lukavetzki Brunn, No. 174, 16in. high. £690

A small ebony-veneered quarter-repeating alarm bracket timepiece, the 6in. dial signed Jam: Cuff London, 13½in. high. £2,310

An ebony quarter-repeating bracket clock, the 7in. dial signed Henry Callowe, 15½in. high. £10,450

Late 17th century ebony veneered quarter-repeating bracket clock, signed I. Lowndes, London, 14½in. high. £4,000

BRACKET CLOCKS
EBONISED

George III ebonised bracket clock, dial signed by Wm. Hughes, London, 14in. high.   £3,750

A small early 18th century Italian ebonised alarm bracket timepiece, 15in. high.   £1,226

An early George III ebonised bracket clock, the 7in. dial signed Jno. Harrison Newcastle, 18in. high.   £935

An ebonised quarter repeating bracket clock, the 7in. dial signed J. Windmills London, 15½in. high.   £2,200

George I ebonised quarter-repeating bracket clock by Joseph Antram, London, 18in. high.   £3,250

An ebony veneered month bracket clock, the 8½in. dial signed Jonathan Puller, Londini Fecit, 14½in. high excluding later feet.   £16,500

An ebony quarter striking bracket clock, the 7in. dial signed Wm. Speakman London, 14in. high.   £2,310

A small ebonised bracket clock, the 6in. dial signed Josiah Emery London, 14½in. high.   £3,300

A small ebony veneered quarter-repeating bracket clock, the 6¼in. dial signed Joseph Knibb, London, 12in. high.   £14,300

BRACKET CLOCKS
EBONISED

Early Georgian ebonised striking bracket
clock, dial signed Phil.
Constantine, London,
19in. high.   £2,500

A George III ebonised
chiming bracket clock,
backplate signed Eardley Norton, 31in. high.
£1,566

George II ebonised striking bracket clock, signed
Benjn Gray, Just. Vulliamy, London, 13½in.
high.   £4,033

Rare silver mounted ebony
bracket clock with velvet
dial, by John Knibb,
Oxford, 11½in. high.
£25,000

An early George III ebonised striking bracket clock,
the dial signed Robt. &
Peter Higgs, London, 17½in.
high.   £7,560

A George II ebonised grand
sonnerie bracket clock, the
dial signed Thos. Hughes,
London, 9¾in. high.
£5,400

Late 19th century English
ebonised quarter chiming
bracket clock, 29in. high.
£1,620

An 18th century Austrian
ebonised quarter striking
bracket clock with gilt
metal handle, 12in. high.
£1,650

A George III ebonised musical bracket clock, dial signed
Robt. Ramsey London,
24in. high.   £3,780

BRACKET CLOCKS
EBONISED

A George II ebonised striking bracket clock, dial signed Richard Peckover London 513, 17½in. high.   £1,500

A George III ebonised miniature striking bracket clock, signed Williams, 168 Shoreditch on Arabic chapter disc, 14½in. high overall.   £2,640

A late Stuart ebonised striking bracket clock, the dial signed J. Windmills London, 15½in. high.   £5,000

A mid Georgian ebonised striking bracket clock, the dial signed Stepn. Rimbault, London, 19½in. high.   £1,512

A Queen Anne ebonised timepiece bracket clock, signed Fromanteel, London, 14¼in. high.   £2,090

A mid-Georgian ebonised striking bracket clock, the dial signed John Fladgate London, 18½in. high.   £1,404

A Queen Anne ebonised bracket clock, the dial signed Dan. Quare, London, 20in. high.   £9,350

A George III ebonised striking bracket clock, the dial signed George Flashman London, 14in. high.   £964

Late 18th century ebonised striking bracket clock, signed A. Van Eeden, Haarlem, 20in. high.   £1,151

BRACKET CLOCKS
EBONISED

Early George III ebonised bracket clock, dial signed Willm. Allam, London, 14in. high. £4,500

An early silver mounted ebony spring clock, backplate signed Joseph Knibb, 16in. high. £30,000

An ebonised miniature bracket timepiece, dial signed W. Johnson, 9¼in. high. £2,500

A George III ebonised bracket clock, the 7in. dial signed Alexdr. Cumming, London, 18½in. high. £925

A William III ebonised quarter striking bracket clock, with gilt metal handle to ogee basket top, 14in. high, excluding later feet. £1,650

An 18th century ebonised and gilt brass mounted quarter chiming bracket clock, signed Wm. Webster, 52cm. high. £2,900

Small and early ebony veneered quarter-repeating bracket clock by John Ebsworth, London, 13in. high. £3,000

A 19th century bracket clock with 8-day movement, 29½in. high, in an ebonised case. £800

A George III ebonised striking bracket clock for the Spanish market by Higgs y Diego Evans, 18¼in. high. £1,870

BRACKET CLOCKS
EBONISED

A brass mounted eboni-
sed wood bracket clock,
circa 1890, 28½in. high.
£1,375

A Regency ebonised bracket
clock, the dial signed W.
French, Royal Exchange,
London, 40cm. high. £880

A small ebony quarter-
repeating basket-top
bracket clock, signed
Benjamin Bell London,
13½in. high. £2,750

An early 18th century ebonised
bracket clock with brass dial, by
Thomas Gardner, London, 18½in.
high. £1,150

An 18th century ebony and
gilt brass mounted bracket
clock, signed on a cartouche
Cha: Cabrier, London, 57cm.
high. £2,200

An 18th century ebony
bracket clock, signed James
Tregent, Leicester Square,
London, 1ft.5½in. high.
£2,500

A late 17th century ebony
'double six hour' grande
sonnerie bracket clock, the
6½in. square dial now
inscribed Tompion Londini,
35.5cm. high. £9,000

Queen Anne ebonised
quarter-repeating
bracket clock by John
Constantin, London,
15in. high. £2,750

A William III quarter repeating
ebony bracket clock, signed
Claudius Du Chesne, Londini
Fecit, 16½in. high. £10,475

BRACKET CLOCKS
EBONISED

A Charles II ebonised striking bracket clock with 6¾in. sq. dial, backplate signed Nathaniel Hodges, 13¾in. high. £3,520

George III ebonised striking bracket clock by Thos. Grignion, London, 15in. high. £4,000

A George I ebonised striking bracket clock, the dial signed Ed. Bayley London, 19in. high. £1,296

A George II ebonised striking bracket clock, plaque signed Will[m] Morgan London, 21½in. high. £972

A Georgian ebonised bracket clock, signed Tho. Wagstaffe, London, 50cm. high. £1,300

An ebony veneered quarter repeating bracket clock, the dials signed Henry Fish, Royal Exchange London, 17½in. high. £2,860

A Queen Anne ebonised bracket clock, the 6¼in. sq. dial signed James Tunn, London, 15in. high. £1,650

A Charles II ebonised turn-table bracket clock, by E. Bird, London, 19in. high. £7,150

A William III ebonised striking bracket clock with gilt metal repousse basket top, dial signed Cha. Gretton, 14½in. high. £2,750

BRACKET CLOCKS
EBONISED

An early Georgian ebonised bracket timepiece with gilt brass handle, the backplate signed Dan. Quare, London, 12¾in. high. £3,080

A gilt brass mounted ebonised quarter chiming musical bracket clock, signed S. & C. Joyce, London, 31in. high. £2,750

A late Victorian ebonised chiming bracket clock, inscribed Thompson, Ashford, 24in., with later wall bracket. £800

A late 17th century ebony veneered bracket timepiece, by Henry Jones, London, 36cm. high. £3,800

An 18th century ebonised bracket clock, signed S. de Charmes, London, 39cm. high. £1,300

A small early George III ebonised bracket clock, the dial signed Jno. Dwerri-house, 16in. high. £1,320

A Charles II ebonised striking bracket clock, backplate signed R. Pingo Neare The Pallmall, Londini in a lambrequin, 13½in. high. £2,090

An ebonised chiming bracket clock, circa 1880, 25in. high, and a conforming bracket, 10½in. high. £825

An early George III ebonised striking bracket clock with brass handle, dial signed Sam. Toulmin, Strand, London, 18½in. high. £880

BRACKET CLOCKS
FRUITWOOD

A George II fruitwood striking miniature bracket clock with carrying handle, the backplate signed Wm. Hughes, 10in. high. £5,280

A Georgian fruitwood bracket clock, signed on a cartouche Henry Heve, London, 43cm. high. £1,700

A mid 18th century fruitwood case eight-day striking bracket clock, 20½in. high. £1,482

INLAID

A George III satinwood bracket clock, the movement signed Tregent, Strand, London, 21in. high. £2,860

An Edwardian inlaid mahogany chiming bracket clock, circa 1900, 26in. high, with a mahogany bracket, 15in. high. £935

A George IV mahogany lyre-form musical bracket clock, signed Frodsham, London, 37in. high.£4,033

An Edwardian inlaid mahogany mantel or bracket clock, with silvered dial, 16¾in. high. £250

An inlaid balloon bracket clock, signed J. Leroux, London, 18¾in. high. £640

Georgian style inlaid mahogany mantel or bracket clock with 8-day striking movement, the dial inscribed Finnigans Ltd., Manchester, 12½in. high. £260

BRACKET CLOCKS
LACQUERED

A George III scarlet and gold japanned bracket clock, made for the Turkish market, the dial signed Wm. Dunant, London, 22½in. high. £8,640

A Georgian green lacquered bracket clock, signed Stepn. Rimbault, London, 1ft.8in. high. £1,700

A mid Georgian scarlet japanned quarter striking, musical and automaton bracket clock in the style of G. Grendey, 37in. high. £55,000

An early japanned bracket clock case containing a modern German clock, 15½in. high. £550

An 18th century C. European red lacquered quarter chiming bracket clock, the backplate signed Iohan Maurer in Prag, 57cm. high. £5,200

A George II brown japanned bracket clock, dial signed Jn. Cotton London, 16¼in. high. £972

A George II green japanned striking bracket clock, the dial signed Fra Dorrell, London, 18¼in. high. £6,600

An early George III dark japanned musical chiming bracket clock for the Turkish market, dial signed Edward Pistor, London, 23½in. high. £3,520

A scarlet lacquer striking bracket clock, the brass dial signed Jas. Smith, London, 20in. high. £1,074

BRACKET CLOCKS
MAHOGANY

A 19th century Masonic bracket clock, marked Swinden & Sons, Birmingham, in castellated mahogany case, 14½in. high. £200

A George III mahogany bracket clock with calendar and striking automaton, signed A. Butler, 13¼in. high. £2,250

A Regency period mahogany cased eight-day bracket clock with matching bracket, 20in. high. £660

An early George III faded mahogany striking bracket clock, the dial signed Henry Sanderson, 18in. high. £3,520

Late 19th century mahogany 8-day domed bracket clock with silvered dial, 12in. high. £240

A Regency Gothic mahogany bracket clock, the painted dial signed Manners & Sons, Stamford, 21½in. high. £935

A mahogany bracket time-piece, signed Daniel Dickerson, Framlingham, 13in. high. £506

A George III bracket clock by Benjamin Dunkley, with brass dial, the mahogany case with brass carrying handles, 22in. high overall. £400

A mahogany bracket clock, signed Debois & Wheeler, Grays Inn Passage, 17¼in. high. £528

BRACKET CLOCKS
MAHOGANY

A George III style mahogany chiming bracket clock, signed Thwaites & Reed, London, 20in. high. £1,500

A George III mahogany striking bracket clock with brass handle, dial signed John Taylor London, 19½in. high. £1,350

A George III mahogany striking bracket clock, the dial signed Thos, Wagstaffe London, 19in. high. £1,944

A George III mahogany striking bracket clock, signed Eardley Norton, London, 15¾in. high. £6,600

A George II striking mahogany bracket clock, date aperture and plaque signed Tho. Hall, Rumsey, 19½in. high. £1,870

George III mahogany bracket clock, inscribed Wright, watchmaker to the King, 17in. high. £1,000

George III mahogany bracket clock, dial signed Frampton, Bury, 17in. high, sold with mahogany wall bracket. £1,000

A George III mahogany striking bracket clock, dial signed Devereux Bowly, London, 20in. high. £3,300

A George III mahogany bracket clock with alarm, signed John Taylor, London, 54cm. high. £1,100

BRACKET CLOCKS
MAHOGANY

A George III mahogany
striking bracket clock,
the dial signed George
Jefferys Chatham, 21¼in.
high.   £2,000

George III mahogany
bracket clock, dial
signed Vulliamy,
London, 15in. high.
                £2,000

A Regency mahogany
chiming bracket clock,
dial signed Yonge &
Son Strand London,
20in. high.   £1,265

A Regency mahogany bracket
clock, the arched brass dial
signed Aynsth. & Jono.
Thwaites, London, 1ft.6½in.
high.   £2,800

A Georgian mahogany quarter
chiming bracket clock, the
painted dial signed Geo.
Wilkins, Soho, 2ft.2in. high.
                £1,450

A George III mahogany
striking bracket clock, the
dial signed Francis Dorrell
London, 19in. high.
                £2,376

A 19th century mahogany
cased 8-day bracket clock,
the silvered dial signed James
Doig of Edinburgh, 16in. high.
                £180

A Victorian mahogany
bracket clock, the movement
by Streeter & Co., 18 New
Bond Street, London, 15in.
wide, 29in. high.   £1,000

George III mahogany
calendar bracket clock,
dial signed Juan y
Melchor Brockbank,
London, 20in. high.
                £2,250

BRACKET CLOCKS
MAHOGANY

A late George II mahogany quarter-repeating bracket clock, the 6½in. dial signed Dan. Torin, Lon., 17in. high. £1,815

A Regency 8-day striking twin fusee bracket clock in figured mahogany case, signed on dial Loof of Tunbridge Wells. £480

A George III Irish mahogany quarter-repeating alarm bracket timepiece, dial signed Chris. Clarke Dublin, 14½in. high. £1,750

A Victorian mahogany chiming bracket clock with chime/silent and selection of 8-bell or Westminster chime, 26in. high. £1,760

Late 18th century George III mahogany bracket clock for the Canadian market, signed Fras. Dumoulin a Montreal, 16½in. high including handle. £1,842

An 18th century mahogany bracket clock, the arched brass dial signed Sidney Smith, Sedgley, 48cm. high. £1,300

A George III mahogany bracket timepiece, signed in the arch Perigal, Coventry Street, London, 26cm. high. £1,050

Early 19th century George III mahogany striking bracket clock, signed Edw. Tomlin, Royal Exchange, London, 15½in. high. £1,535

A George III mahogany bracket clock, the arched brass dial signed Benjn. Ward, London, 52cm. high. £3,000

BRACKET CLOCKS
MAHOGANY

A mahogany cased eight day striking bracket clock, engraved Joseph Green, London, 21½in. high. **£850**

Early 19th century Chinese mahogany bracket clock with striking automaton, 26¼in. high. **£2,200**

George III mahogany striking bracket clock, dial signed John Lloyd, London, 19in. **£2,000**

A George III mahogany striking bracket clock, by Ellicott, London, 16in. high. **£2,200**

A Regency mahogany striking bracket clock, the painted dial signed Collett, Chelsea, 15½in. high. **£1,080**

A Regency mahogany and gilt brass mounted bracket clock, the brass dial signed Robt. Wood, London, 43cm. high. **£1,200**

A mahogany bracket clock of pagoda form, the movement inscribed Robert Roskell & Son, Liverpool, 21in. high. **£400**

A mahogany veneered bracket clock, signed in the arch Richd. Ward, Winchester, 18½in. high. **£1,705**

A late Georgian mahogany musical bracket clock, chime/not chime lever signed Rivers & Son, Cornhill, London, 24in. high. **£3,024**

BRACKET CLOCKS MAHOGANY

A George III mahogany striking bracket clock, the silvered dial signed James Wild London, 16in. high.　£1,836

A Regency period mahogany and brass bracket clock, dial signed Thomas Pace, London, 19in. high. £940

A mahogany bracket clock by Charles Frodsham, 24in. high, circa 1850.　£400

A George II mahogany striking bracket clock with brass handle, signed Benj. Ward London, 18½in. high. £2,808

A George III mahogany bracket clock, the circular enamel dial signed Biddell, London, 53cm. high.　£1,400

A Regency mahogany and brass bound bracket clock by Handley & Moore, London, 17½in. high.　£950

A Regency mahogany bracket clock, Gothic shaped case, by Payne, London, 24in. high.　£1,250

A George III mahogany bracket clock, dial signed Tomlin Royal Exchange London, 13in. high.　£1,540

A mahogany chiming musical bracket clock, the 8in. dial signed John Taylor London, 24in. high.　£2,200

BRACKET CLOCKS
MARQUETRY

A marquetry bracket clock, probably English provincial, circa 1700, 14in. high.   £2,500

A George III Vernis Martin bracket timepiece, signed Isaac Rogers, London, 25in. high.   £4,000

A rosewood and marquetry bracket clock, dial signed Evershed & Son, Brighton, circa 1890, 19¾in. high.   £1,100

METAL

19th century French brass and champleve enamel bracket clock.   £650

Small George III gilt metal bracket clock, signed Henry Favre, London, 7½in. high.   £5,000

A gilt metal automaton quarter-striking and musical bracket clock for the Chinese market, circa 1800, 9in. high.   £3,130

OAK

An oak bracket clock, dial signed James McCabe, 8½in. high.   £1,320

A Victorian pollard oak Gothic Revival bracket clock, the dial signed Muller, Twickenham, 42in. high.   £700

A bracket clock with eight-day striking movement, by Thompson, Ashford, 24in. high, in an oak case. £280

BRACKET CLOCKS
RED WALNUT

A mid Georgian mahogany or red walnut striking bracket clock with brass handle, 19in. high.   £1,188

RELIGIEUSE

A Louis XIV ebony and boulle religieuse with ormolu dial, 16½in. wide.   £1,728

ROSEWOOD

A Regency rosewood and brass inlaid mantel timepiece, the silvered dial signed Carpenter, London, 9½in. high.   £1,900

A red walnut quarter repeating bracket clock, signed on the chapter ring Asselin, London, 19in. high.   £935

A documentary Louis XIV bronze mounted tortoiseshell religieuse, signed Gaudron a Paris, the case inscribed L.B., circa 1710, 18in. high.   £3,837

A rosewood bracket timepiece, signed Wm. Speakman, London, 20½in. high. £236

A George III mahogany or red walnut striking bracket clock, the plaque signed Yeldrae Notron London 1053, 18in. high.   £1,296

An ebonised pendule religieuse, signed Nicolas Brodon, Paris, circa 1680, 18in. high.   £3,036

A Regency period bracket clock, the brass inlaid lancet case of Egyptian styling, circa 1810, 20in. high.   £1,300

BRACKET CLOCKS
ROSEWOOD

Victorian rosewood cased bracket clock, inlaid with brass floral decoration.
£1,100

A rosewood bracket clock with movement by Yonge & Son of the Strand, 11in. high.
£2,500

An eight-day movement bracket clock, by Wm. Alexander, 22in. high, 1828-44.
£750

A French 18th century gilt brass mounted and inlaid rosewood bracket clock, signed Jean Tolly a Paris, 36in. high.
£1,045

A 19th century rosewood and inlaid bracket timepiece, 32cm. high.
£520

An early 19th century rosewood bracket clock by B. Lautier of Bath, 43cm. high.
£1,900

TORTOISESHELL

A George III tortoiseshell striking bracket clock, the dial signed Geo. Clarke London, 17in. high.
£2,500

A tortoiseshell bracket clock, dial signed G. Yonge & Son, 13½in. high.
£1,500

A Continental tortoiseshell bracket timepiece, basically circa 1700, 16in. high.
£1,540

BRACKET CLOCKS
WALNUT

A gilt brass mounted walnut quarter chiming bracket clock, 32¾in. high.   £660

A George II walnut striking bracket clock, signed Cha. Blanchard, London, 19in. high.   £2,250

A walnut quarter repeating bracket clock with 7½in. brass dial, backplate signed Jacob Massy, London, 17in. high.
£2,000

A walnut chiming bracket clock, the three train fusee movement striking quarter hours on 8 bells or four gongs, 15in. high.   £1,320

A Regency walnut cased bracket clock with silvered dial, maker Raw Bros., London.   £385

An 18th century bracket clock in burr walnut case, with eight-day movement by Jos. Kirk, 16in. high.
£1,850

A Victorian walnut bracket clock, the case in Gothic style, 2ft.2in. high.   £400

A walnut bracket clock, signed Robt. Allam, London, 47cm. high.
£1,078

A walnut chiming bracket clock, by Viner London, No. 2208, 22in. high, and a walnut bracket, 8in. high.
£660

CALENDAR CLOCKS

Rosewood cased double dial calendar clock, by L.G. & W.W. Carter Bristol, Connecticut, circa 1865, 30¼in. high. £430

A French red marble perpetual calendar mantel clock and barometer, 18½in. high. £770

An Ithaca walnut calendar clock, 1866, 45in. long. £1,032

An oak double dial calendar clock, by Waterbury Clock Co., circa 1900, 29in. long. £850

A Belgian incised black slate perpetual calendar mantel clock, 16¾in. high. £770

A walnut calendar timepiece, by New Haven Clock Co., circa 1900, 32in. long. £350

French calendar mantel clock by A. Redier, in a rectangular ebonised wood case, circa 1880, 13¼in. high. £333

A walnut mantel clock, the movement of the Black Forest type with wooden plates, 17in. high. £375

Late 19th century oak double dial calendar shelf clock, by Waterbury Clock Co., 24in. high. £430

CALENDAR CLOCKS

A Restoration rosewood month calendar mantel regulator with a glass dome, 24in. high. £26,400

Late 19th century French porcelain mounted ormolu mantel clock with perpetual calendar, 17in. high. £2,380

A gilt bronze perpetual calendar mantel clock, circa 1860, 21in. high. £2,100

A walnut double dial calendar shelf clock, by Seth Thomas Clock Co., 32in. high. £1,160

A Victorian eight-day calendar clock by B. Jacobs, Hull, 15¾in. wide. £400

A grain-painted astronomical calendar clock, by Gabs Patent Welch Spring & Co., circa 1880, 30½in. long. £2,635

An ormolu and white marble four glass clock with perpetual calendar and moonphase dial below time dial, 16¾in. high. £3,740

A French black marble and porphyry perpetual calendar mantel clock, signed Francis Glading, 15¼in. high. £1,045

A late 19th century oak double dial calendar shelf clock, by Waterbury Clock Co., 29in. high. £390

CARRIAGE CLOCKS
BAMBOO

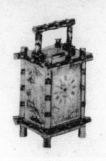

A French porcelain panel-led 'bamboo' carriage clock, 7in. high.　£1,650

Chinese design carriage clock with mock bamboo frame.　£1,250

A late 19th century French carriage clock in gilt 'bamboo' chinoiserie case, inscribed John Bennett, Paris, 8in. high.　£1,250

ENAMEL

French carriage clock in brass and champleve enamel case.　£2,500

A silver gilt and enamel miniature 'carriage clock', 1¾in. high.　£864

French brass and champleve enamel carriage clock in Corniche type case, 7in. high.　£750

A champleve enamelled brass carriage clock with cut compensated balance to lever platform, 7in. high.　£2,700

A quarter-repeating and cloisonne enamel carriage clock, 3in. high.　£3,300

A gilt metal and enamel striking carriage clock, ivorine dials within multi-coloured champleve enamel mask, 7in. high.　£2,530

CARRIAGE CLOCKS
ENAMEL FACE

An alarm carriage clock, the dial signed Bolviller A Paris, 7in. high. £1,000

An enamel-mounted carriage clock with black enamel dial, 4½in. high. £1,000

An enamel-mounted carriage clock, 6½in. high, with a travelling case. £1,190

A Liberty & Co. pewter and enamel clock, circa 1905. £220

Lacquered brass and enamel striking carriage clock, 6½in. high. £1,000

A repeating gilt brass carriage clock, circa 1890, 6½in. high. £1,460

A carriage clock with an enamel dial, 5¼in. high, and a gilt metal stand, 1¾in. high. £850

Small enamel mounted carriage timepiece, stamped Margaine, 3¼in. high. £2,000

A French brass carriage timepiece with cylinder movement, in a plain pillared case, 6in. high. £240

CARRIAGE CLOCKS
ENAMEL FACE

French late 19th century enamelled brass and glass repeating carriage clock, by Tiffany & Co., 6¾in. high. £1,265

Glass and brass carriage timepiece, probably Boston, circa 1890, 7in. high. £325

A gilt metal grande sonnerie carriage clock with enamel dial, case with stamp of Henri Jacot, 7in. high. £1,782

Gilt metal and enamel quarter-striking carriage clock with foliate handle, 6in. high. £1,500

A quarter-striking carriage clock, the enamel dial signed Dent 33 Cockspur Street, London, 6in. high. £1,500

A gilt metal striking carriage clock with enamel dial, 5¼in. high. £865

A gilt brass and enamel striking carriage clock with uncut bimetallic balance to silvered lever platform, 5½in. high. £1,320

An English carriage clock, enamel dial signed Dent London, 8¾in. high. £4,000

A lacquered brass miniature carriage clock with cylinder platform, 3in. high. £1,250

CARRIAGE CLOCKS
OVAL CASE

Gilt metal grande son-
nerie oval carriage clock
in engraved case with
scrolling handle, 6in.
high.   £1,026

Aneroid barometer of
carriage clock form,
signed R. & J. Beck,
London, 3¼in. high.
£280

A gilt metal striking oval
carriage clock for the Oriental market, stamp of Japy
Freres, 6in. high.   £1,320

A gilt metal grande sonnerie
oval carriage clock with
enamel dial, 6.1/8in. high.
£1,760

A gilt metal striking oval
carriage clock with scroll
handle and on rosso
antiquo marble stand,
5½in. high, excluding stand.
£1,430

A gilt metal striking oval
carriage clock with uncut
bimetallic balance to silvered lever platform, plain
oval case, 5½in. high.
£605

A silvered brass oval miniature carriage clock, the case
with stamp of A. Margaine,
8cm. high.   £290

An oval engraved gilt brass
grande sonnerie carriage clock,
7½in. high.   £1,688

A miniature oval carriage
timepiece with white enamel
dial, 3in. high.   £440

CARRIAGE CLOCKS
PORCELAIN MOUNTED

A porcelain mounted carriage clock, the dial with a gilt chapter ring, 6¼in. high. £1,500

Brass striking and repeating pillared carriage clock set with Art Nouveau porcelain panels £750

A porcelain mounted alarm carriage clock, the repeating lever movement with gong striking, 6¼in. high. £1,200

A French gilt brass carriage clock, the lever movement striking on a gong, 21cm. high. £920

A porcelain panelled carriage clock, the movement with the trademark of J. Dejardin, 7in. high. £2,550

A 19th century French gilt brass and porcelain mounted grande sonnerie carriage clock, with trademark P.M., 18cm. high. £4,600

A porcelain mounted alarm carriage clock, the dial signed G. C. Shreve & Co., San Francisco, 6¼in. high. £1,000

A gilt brass porcelain mounted striking carriage clock with porcelain dial, stamp of Achille Brocot, 6¼in. high. £1,870

A porcelain mounted carriage clock, the dial and side panels with scenes of Harlequin and Columbine, 5¾in. high. £500

CARRIAGE CLOCKS
PORCELAIN MOUNTED

A bronzed brass porcelain mounted striking carriage clock with 'Sevres' porcelain dial, 6.1/8in. high. £2,250

A porcelain mounted carriage clock, the repeating lever movement stamped Maurice et Cie, 5½in. high. £880

Porcelian mounted carriage clock, dial signed J. W. Benson, London, 8½in. high, backplate stamped Drocourt. £6,820

Late 19th century gilt bronze and jewelled porcelain carriage clock in engraved gorge case, 7in. high. £2,145

A gilt metal porcelain mounted carriage clock with lever platform, the case with stamp of Japy Freres, 9½in. high. £3,350

A 19th century French gilt brass and porcelain mounted carriage clock, 18cm. high. £2,100

A porcelain mounted alarm carriage clock in a gorge case, 5½in. high. £2,500

A French gilt brass carriage clock, the dial and side panels decorated with scenes of young couples, 7in. high. £850

A gilt brass porcelain mounted striking carriage clock, the dial and side panels painted in the Sevres style, 5½in. high. £3,300

CARRIAGE CLOCKS
ROUND FACE

French gilt brass carriage clock by Pierre and Alfred Drocourt, with white enamel dial, 16cm. high. £750

An inlaid horn miniature carriage timepiece with 9ct. gold handle, feet and scrolls, London, 1908, by Wm. Comyns, 2½in. high. £255

A Richard & Co. petite sonnerie repeating carriage clock with fluted handle, 7½in. high £750

Lacquered brass petite sonnerie small sized carriage clock with split bimetallic balance to silvered lever platform, 4¼in. high. £810

A brass calendar carriage timepiece, enamel dial with chapter disc above gilt mask, 4¾in. high. £220

A brass and glass panelled carriage clock, dial inscribed 'Aird & Thomson, Glasgow', 5½in. high. £340

A lacquered brass striking carriage clock with enamel dial with engine-turned gilt mask, gorge case, stamp of Drocourt, 5¾in. high. £760

A Swiss gilt brass striking carriage clock with chronometer escapement, circa 1830, 7in. high. £6,524

A gold mounted tortoiseshell miniature carriage timepiece, maker's mark CD, 1906, 9.5cm. high. £902

CARRIAGE CLOCKS
ROUND FACE

A carriage clock with a dished silvered chapter ring, the movement stamped Maurice et Cie, 5¼in. high, with a leather travelling case.   £650

Silvered brass and glass carriage timepiece, probably Boston, circa 1890, 6½in. high.   £180

French brass repeat alarm carriage clock by Pierre and Alfred Drocourt, 6in. high.
£750

A gilt metal grande sonnerie carriage clock with strike/ repeat on gongs with selection lever in the base, 6¼in. high.   £1,404

An English striking carriage clock, mottled plates signed Chas. Frodsham, 9in. high.
£5,184

A French brass carriage clock, the movement with lever escapement, 6in. high. £319

A small carriage timepiece, the 1in. dial signed Payne London, 3in. high.   £990

A lacquered brass striking carriage clock, the movement with lever platform, 6½in. high.   £486

A gilt metal striking carriage clock, the dial with concave ivory Arabic chapter, the case with stamp of Drocourt, 6¾in. high.   £756

53

CARRIAGE CLOCKS
ROUND FACE

A brass quarter-striking calendar carriage clock, 7in. high.   £1,000

Glass and brass carriage timepiece, probably Boston, circa 1890, 6¼in. high.   £250

A French 19th century gilt brass carriage clock, the lever movement striking on a gong and bearing the Drocourt trademark, 7in. high.   £850

Grande sonnerie alarm carriage clock, dial signed Chas. Frodsham, London, 6in. high.   £1,750

A small quarter-striking alarm carriage clock, dial signed Breguet, 4½in. high, and a leather travelling case.   £805

A grande sonnerie striking carriage clock, the white enamel dial signed A. Jackemann, Paris, 6in. high.   £1,320

A lacquered brass striking carriage clock, the ivorine dial with gilt mask, cannelee riche case, stamped for Henri Jacot, 6in. high.   £490

An English gilt metal carriage clock, movement signed Barwise London, 6in. high.   £800

A grande sonnerie carriage clock, the base with the stamp of Henri Jacot, 7in. high.   £990

CARRIAGE CLOCKS
ROUND FACE

French gilt brass and glass
repeating carriage clock,
circa 1900, 7¼in. high.
£725

Chronometer carriage
clock by Dent, London,
dial signed, 7in. high.
£10,000

Late 19th century Ameri-
can brass and glass carriage
timepiece with eight-day
movement, 9.1/8in. high.
£185

A gilt metal striking carriage
clock, inscribed Examined
by Dent and with presentation inscription dated 1877,
7in. high.   £528

Late 19th century French
brass repeating alarm carriage
clock, the dial signed E.
Caldwell & Co., Philadelphia,
7½in. high.   £780

A 19th century French gilt
brass carriage clock, the lever
movement striking on a gong
with push repeat, 19cm. high.
£550

Large carriage clock with
enamel dial, movement
stamped Drocourt, 8½in.
high.   £2,500

English carriage timepiece,
dial signed Adams, Lon-
don, 9in. high, in leather
case.   £1,750

A 19th century French gilt
brass carriage clock, the
backplate bearing the
Drocourt trademark, 6½in.
high.   £950

CARRIAGE CLOCKS
ROUND FACE

A lacquered brass minia-
ture carriage clock with
silvered lever platform,
3in. high.   £650

Gilt and silvered brass
timepiece carriage clock
by Payne, London, 5½in.
high.   £750

A lacquered brass repeating
carriage clock with gilt
metal Shakespearian panels,
movement signed Army and
Navy, Paris, 7¾in. high.
£3,000

A gilt metal striking carriage
clock with decorative swagged
Arabic chaptered enamel dial,
6½in. high.   £440

A silver plated striking carriage
clock with split compensated
balance to gilt lever platform,
6½in. high.   £605

A brass carriage timepiece,
the movement with cylin-
der escapement, 6¼in.
high.   £200

A brass grande sonnerie
striking carriage clock,
gorge case, stamp of Dro-
court, 6in. high.   £1,404

A gilt brass grande sonnerie
carriage clock, 7¾in. high.
£1,535

English gilt metal car-
riage clock, signed
Bloomsbury, London,
4¾in. high.   £800

CARRIAGE CLOCKS
ROUND FACE

A gilt brass striking carriage clock, the backplate stamped J. Klaftenburger, 5¼in. high. £1,870

French glass and brass carriage timepiece, dial signed Mappin & Webb Ltd., Paris, circa 1900, 6½in. high. £140

A gilt brass carriage clock with engraved side panels, signed Paul Buhre, St. Petersburg, the movement by F.-A. Margaine, 7in. high. £2,016

A gilt metal striking carriage clock with silvered lever platform, the gilt chapter ring signed Leroy Paris, 6¼in. high. £490

A 19th century French gilt brass carriage clock, signed on the back plate E. Dent, Paris, 944, 5½in. high. £1,850

A lacquered brass grande sonnerie giant carriage clock, 8¼in. high. £1,404

An English chronometer carriage timepiece, by Dent, London, with mahogany carrying case, 8½in. high. £7,150

English carriage clock by Smith & Sons, London, 9in. high. £1,500

A 19th century French brass carriage clock, the lever movement striking on a gong with alarm and push repeat, 7½in. high. £1,300

CARRIAGE CLOCKS
ROUND FACE

An alarm carriage clock, the enamel dial signed James Muirhead & Son, Glasgow, 6¾in. high. £1,600

A grande sonnerie calendar carriage clock cum barometer, the barometer inscribed R. W. Inglis 1897, 6½in. high. £2,200

Late 19th century gilt brass carriage clock with fluted pillars, 7in. high. £300

A 19th century French gilt brass grande sonnerie carriage clock, the lever movement striking on two gongs with push repeat, 20cm. high. £1,400

A small minute-repeating mantel or travelling time-piece signed Cole London. 3¾in. high. £660

A petite-sonnerie repeating and alarm carriage clock, with Arabic numerals and signed A H Rodanet, Paris, 6in. high. £770

A chronometer carriage clock signed M. F. Dent, 8½in. high. £10,000

A 19th century French ormolu carriage clock, the lever movement striking on a gong with push repeat and alarm, 8½in. high. £750

A grande sonnerie carriage clock, the base plate with the stamp of A. Brocot, 5¾in. high. £990

CARRIAGE CLOCKS
ROUND TOP

A silver and shagreen miniature travelling timepiece, the enamel dial signed W. Thornhill & Co., Paris, 3in. high.   £250

An early Victorian gilt metal carriage clock, case in the manner of T. Cole, 11½in. high.   £2,376

A brass cased quarter striking carriage clock, the backplate signed L. Leroy & Cie, 6in. high.   £864

A silver calendar carriage clock, the silver dial with gold Breguet hands, the backplate signed Jump, 6¼in. high.   £18,700

Breguet Neveu & Compie., No. 3992: a silver quarter striking carriage clock with alarm, 5½in. high.   £23,100

A shagreen carriage clock of humpback form, dial signed Jump Paris 93 Mount Street (London), 7in. high.   £935

SILVERED DIAL

French brass carriage clock by Francois-Arsene Margaine, with circular silvered dial, 7in. high.   £500

A gilt brass grande-sonnerie calendar carriage clock with uncut compensated balance to the silvered lever platform, stamp of Drocourt, 6½in. high.   £3,850

Gilt metal travelling or mantel timepiece with arched silver dial, 5¼in. high.   £750

CARRIAGE CLOCKS
SILVERED DIAL

A French brass grande sonnerie carriage alarm clock, 7¼in. high. £375

An English brass carriage timepiece, dial signed Barwise, London, 7¼in. £750

Gilt metal carriage clock by J. & A. Jump, London, 4½in. high. £2,750

An early multi-piece striking carriage clock with narrow lever platform, strike and alarm on bell, 5¾in. high. £540

A 19th century English time-piece, the backplate signed French, Royal Exchange, London, 17.5cm. high. £5,200

A gilt brass quarter striking carriage clock with uncut compensated balance to lever platform, 5in. high. £605

A gilt metal striking carriage clock by Paul Garnier, one-piece case with lifting front glass, 5in. high. £1,430

A 19th century English gilt brass quarter striking carriage clock, the dial signed James McCabe, Royal Exchange, London 2677, 19cm. high. £3,000

A fine early English fusee carriage clock with silvered dial, by G. & W. Yonge, London, 5½in. high. £1,000

CARRIAGE CLOCKS
WHITE FACE

Early French brass carriage clock, signed Hy Marc, Paris, 8in. high. £750

English brass carriage clock, inscribed Mappin & Webb. £165

A French carriage clock with morocco travelling case and key, by F. A. Margaine, Paris, 6in. high. £400

A lacquered brass grande sonnerie carriage clock with calendar, by Drocourt, No. 12276, 7in. high. £1,842

A gilt brass bottom-wind striking carriage clock with split bimetallic balance to silvered lever platform, dial signed Leroy et fils 5½in. high. £528

A brass quarter striking carriage clock signed 7669 Leroy & Fils Palais Royal 13-15 Paris, 5¼in. high. £702

A French brass carriage timepiece, the enamel dial signed Leroy & Fils, in a gorge case, 9.5cm. high. £440

A gilt metal striking carriage clock for the Chinese market, stamp of Japy Freres, 5¾in. high. £715

A gilt metal early multipiece carriage clock signed Leroy a Paris on backplate, 5in. high. £345

CARRIAGE CLOCKS
WHITE FACE

A 19th century French gilt brass carriage clock, bearing the Jacot trademark on the backplate, 6¾in. high. £780

A grande sonnerie alarm carriage clock, dial signed Leroy & Fils , 5¾in. high. £1,100

Brass one-piece carriage clock, enamel dial signed no. 1 Hy Marc, Paris, 5¾in. high. £500

An English petit sonnerie carriage clock with white enamel dial inscribed Lund & Blockley, 6in. high. £1,900

A 19th century French brass carriage clock, the lever movement striking on a gong, with push repeat and with the Margaine trademark on the backplate, 7¼in. high. £520

A 19th century French brass carriage clock, signed on the backplate Ollivant & Botsford, Paris & Manchester, 17cm. high. £320

A French brass carriage clock, the lever movement striking on a gong, 4¾in. high. £150

An ornate gilt repeating carriage clock, signed Bolviller a Paris, 6¼in. high. £715

A 19th century French brass carriage clock, 7in. high, together with a leather travelling case. £500

CARRIAGE CLOCKS
WHITE FACE

A gilt metal striking carriage clock with centre seconds for the Chinese market, 6in. high. £715

An early multi-piece gilt carriage clock by Paul Garnier, 5¾in. high. £2,600

A 19th century French gilt brass miniature carriage timepiece, the lever movement with enamel dial, 3¾in. high, together with a travelling case. £880

A 19th century French gilt brass carriage clock, the lever movement striking on a bell with alarm, 6¼in. high. £220

A French 19th century gilt brass carriage clock, bearing the Drocourt trademark, and signed for Klaftenberger, Paris, 17cm. high. £340

Victorian carriage clock with cloisonne panels, 1860. £185

A 19th century French gilt brass carriage clock, the enamel dial signed for J. F. Bautte, Geneve, 17cm. high. £2,000

A 19th century brass carriage clock with petit sonnerie and alarm movement, the enamel dial signed Dent, Paris, 4½in. high. £610

A 19th century French brass carriage clock, the lever movement with petite sonnerie, the dial signed for Dent London, 7in. high. £900

63

CARRIAGE CLOCKS
WHITE FACE

A lacquered brass grande
sonnerie calendar carriage
clock, signed by Emmanuel,
6¾in. high.   £2,500

A brass cased French
carriage clock with
white enamel face and
cylinder escapement.
£150

An eight-day repeating
carriage clock with
alarm, inscribed 'Repasse
par Leroy & Fils'. 14 cm.
£750

A gilt metal striking
carriage clock, stamp of
Henri Jacot, 5¾in. high.
£880

A lacquered brass petite
sonnerie carriage clock with
enamel dial, corniche case,
5¼in. high.   £605

A petite sonnerie and
alarm carriage clock, the
white enamel dial inscribed
'Dent 61, Strand, London'.
18 cm. high. £1,000

A gilt metal striking one-
piece carriage clock, the
backplate stamped in an
oval Hy. Marc Paris, 6¾in.
high.   £756

A gilt brass striking carriage
clock, stamp of Henri Jacot,
5½in. high.   £626

A gilt metal one-piece grande
sonnerie carriage clock with
bridge to helical spring of
'jewelled' lever platform,
probably Franche Comte,
5½in. high.   £1,188

CARRIAGE CLOCKS
WHITE FACE

Gilt metal petite sonn-
erie carriage clock,
enamel dial inscribed
Dent, London, 6¼in.
high.   £750

A miniature French gilt
brass carriage timepiece,
with the trade stamp of
Henri Jacot, 3¾in. high.
£253

A gilt brass grande sonnerie
carriage clock, 7½in. high,
including handle.   £874

A gilt metal striking carriage clock with dial
signed Lucien Paris,
6¼in. high.   £594

An English quarter-strik-
ing carriage clock, dial
signed James McCabe,
9¼in. high.   £15,000

A gilt brass quarter striking
carriage clock with cut
bimetallic balance to lever
platform, 6in. high. £550

A gilt metal striking carriage
clock with modern lever
platform, stamp of Henri
Jacot, 4¾in. high.   £660

A brass one-piece striking
carriage clock by Paul
Garnier Hger. De La
Marine A Paris, 6¼in. high.
£1,296

A lacquered brass grande
sonnerie carriage clock,
7in. high.   £921

CARRIAGE CLOCKS
WHITE FACE

A brass carriage clock, by T. Hyde, Sleaford, in ornate case. £130

A lacquered brass carriage clock, signed on the dial in cyrillic, A. M. Geracimov, St. Petersburg, 8in. high. £806

A French brass carriage clock, by Francois Arsene Margaine, 6½in. high. £550

A brass striking carriage clock, enamel dial inscribed Leroy & Fils 57 New Bond Street Made in France, 5½in. high. £400

A 19th century French brass carriage clock, signed on the backplate Bolviller A Paris, 7in. high. £520

A gilt brass carriage clock with calendar and alarm, circa 1845, 7½in. high. £941

A silvered and parcel gilt grande sonnerie calendar carriage clock, 7¼in. high. £2,160

A brass grande sonnerie carriage clock with split compensated balance to lever platform, 5¾in. high. £660

A French gilt brass and white metal grande sonnerie alarm carriage clock, 7½in. high. £900

CARRIAGE CLOCKS
WHITE FACE

Late 19th century gilt brass repeating carriage alarm clock with white enamel dial, 7¼in. high. £385

A lacquered brass one-piece striking carriage clock, the backplate stamped Hy. Marc Paris, 5½in. high. £486

A brass striking carriage clock with strike/repeat on gong, stamp of Henri Jacot, 4.7/8in. high. £400

A lacquered brass petite sonnerie carriage clock, with the trademark of Francois-Arsene Margaine, 7in. high. £1,008

A Franche Comte gilt metal striking carriage clock for the Chinese market, 6½in. high. £1,000

A gilt brass carriage clock with gilt platform to lever escapement, 6¾in. high, including handle. £550

A 19th century French brass carriage clock, the lever movement with quarter striking on two gongs, 7in. high. £360

A 19th century French brass carriage clock, the lever movement striking on a gong with alarm and bearing the Drocourt trademark, 16.5cm. high. £520

An Austrian brass grande sonnerie carriage clock with calendar, 5½in. high. £1,620

CARRIAGE CLOCKS
WHITE FACE

French glass and brass repeating carriage clock, circa 1900, dial marked Dent, 6½in. high. £345

A French carriage clock with lever escapement and repeat mechanism and porcelain dial. £220

A grande sonnerie alarm carriage clock, the movement stamped Fumey, 7½in. high. £1,470

A gilt metal striking miniature carriage clock with enamel dial, 3¼in. high. £864

A singing bird carriage clock, the backplate stamped Japy Freres, 11in. high. £3,000

A 19th century French miniature brass carriage timepiece, the lever movement bearing the Margaine trademark, 9.5cm. high. £400

WOODEN

Rosewood carriage clock by Jas. Murray & Co., London, with brass drop carrying handle, 10¾in. high. £1,500

A Victorian brass inlaid, rosewood carriage clock, dial signed Craighead & Webb, 9¼in. high. £1,540

A satinwood four glass striking carriage clock, the dial signed Arnold & Dent London No 408, 8¾in. high. £3,456

CARTEL CLOCKS

A George II giltwood cartel clock, signed James Smyth, London, circa 1750, 30in. high.   £1,666

A George III giltwood cartel clock with later white dial and timepiece movement, 30in. high.   £880

A George III giltwood cartel timepiece with single fusee movement, 35in. high.   £550

Late 18th/early 19th century French giltwood cartel clock, 28in. high.   £660

Louis XVI ormolu cartel clock, dial signed Imbert, 36½in. high.   £1,000

A Louis XVI ormolu cartel clock, the enamel dial signed Brille a Paris, 14in. high.   £4,400

Regency style gilt bronze cartel clock, dial signed Breguet A Paris, circa 1880, 71cm. high.   £750

A French cartel clock with eight day movement, 9½in. high.   £120

A George III giltwood cartel clock with associated silvered dial signed Wm. Linderby, London, 34in. high. £3,080

CARTEL CLOCKS

Gilt bronze cartel wall
clock in waisted case,
circa 1870, 22¾in. high.
£600

Louis XVI style French
bronze cartel clock in reti-
culated rococo scroll-sha-
ped case, 23in. high.
£342

A wall-hanging cartel
clock in a rococo case
of gilt bronze, 2ft. 6in.
high, by Clouzier of
Paris.   £5,000

Gilt bronze cartel wall
clock, with pendulum,
circa 1850, 32in. high.
£950

A wall clock, by Sewill (maker
to the Royal Navy), Liverpool,
40in. high.   £250

A 19th century French
Dore bronze cartel clock,
27in. high.   £1,260

An ormolu cartel clock of
Louis XVI style, the enamel
dial signed Guibal, Paris,
26in. high.   £495

A Louis XVI ormolu cartel
clock, the enamel dial signed
Charles Leroy a Paris, 13in.
high.   £1,296

Louis XV gilt bronze
cartel clock, signed
Gilbert a Paris, circa
1760, 29in. high.
£7,500

CARTEL CLOCKS

Louis XV gilt bronze cartel clock, signed Lepaute Hger. du Roy, circa 1755, 43in. high. £17,500

19th century French ormolu wall clock with an 8in. dial and eight day movement. £1,000

A George III giltwood cartel timepiece, the dial signed Robt. Mawley London, 25½in. high. £2,500

Louis XV ormolu cartel clock, signed Joannes Biesta Paris, 33in. high. £2,500

A Continental striking cartel clock with white enamel face, overall length 25½in. £620

A Louis XVI cartel clock, the dial signed Charles Le Roy a Paris, 37in. high. £3,240

An 18th century Continental carved giltwood cartel clock, 64cm. high. £780

A 19th century gilt cartel clock by Mynuel, Paris. £1,300

An early 19th century French ormolu cased wall clock with eight-day movement, 30in. high, overall. £1,000

CHRONOMETERS

A two day marine chronometer contained in mahogany deck box, diam. of bezel 115mm. £4,000

A marine chronometer in a brass mounted rosewood case, the lid with a separate glass panel, inscribed D. McGregor & Co. £740

A two day marine chronometer by Victor Kullberg, diam. of bezel 123mm. £2,500

An eight-day marine chronometer by Hatton & Harris No. 570, diam. of bezel 133mm. £5,500

An eight-day marine chronometer by John Poole, in brass bound rosewood case, diam. of bezel 142mm. £3,000

An eight-day marine chronometer by James Muirhead & Son, diam. of bezel 143mm., circa 1840. £3,500

A small one-day marine chronometer by John Roger Arnold, the dial 64mm. diam. £2,592

A two-day marine chronometer in two-tier glazed mahogany box, the 4½in. silvered dial with Arabic numerals, signed Thomas Mercer, No. 28271, in travelling box. £462

A two-day marine chronometer, the silvered dial signed James Muirhead, Glasgow, No. 2169, 100mm. diam. of dial. £5,400

CHRONOMETERS

A 36-hour marine chronometer by Leroy No. 821, diam. of bezel 82mm.
£638

A marine chronometer by J. R. Arnold No. 578, diam. of bezel 105mm.
£2,640

A two-day marine chronometer by James Poole No. 5818, diam. of bezel 125mm.
£1,155

A mahogany eight-day mantel chronometer with a 4½in. silvered dial, 8in. high. £1,650

A two-day marine chronometer by Morris Tobias No. 794, diam. of bezel 115mm.
£1,320

An early marine chronometer by John Arnold & Son, with 4½in. circular silvered dial, in mahogany box.
£8,000

Late 19th century coromandel and brass inlaid marine chronometer.
£775

A two-day marine chronometer, the dial signed by Dobbie McInnes Ltd., Glasgow, no. 9615, dial 10cm. diam.
£607

A small two-day marine chronometer by Brockbank & Atkins, in mahogany carrying case, diam. of bezel 100mm. £1,500

CLOCK SETS

A French gilt marble and gilt metal garniture, with matching three-arm candelabra, 18in. high. £1,100

A French ormolu and porcelain mounted three-piece clock garniture, the clock 13in. high, the side pieces 13¾in. high. £475

An unusual 19th century enamelled and gilt brass 'Gothic' chamber clock and candlesticks, clock 22in. high. £3,247

19th century Meissen blue and white clock set by Lund & Blockley, 39in. high. £950

A good ormolu and porcelain garniture, 18in. high. £1,540

A French veined marble garniture, 17in. high. £418

CLOCK SETS

A Second Empire ormolu and green marble clock set on the theme of the Oath of the Horatii, the side pieces formed as ewers. £4,377

A 19th century French ormolu and porcelain clock garniture, the enamel dial signed Lenoir a Paris, 1ft.8½in. high, together with a matching pair of three branch candelabra. £1,900

19th century Sevres porcelain garniture de cheminee, by S. Wartenberg, Paris. £2,000

A pale Royal rouge marble and ormolu three-piece clock set, the lidded urn holding the clock, with two four-branch, four light candelabra, all 34in. high. £6,200

A 19th century French ormolu clock garniture, the clock contained in a drum, 2ft.9in. high, together with matching pair of seven branch candelabra, 2ft.10in. high. £1,800

A white marble and gilt metal three-piece clock set, by J. Marti & Cie., the clock 23in. high, the urns 17in. high. £950

CLOCK SETS

Porcelain and gilt bronze composed clock garniture, movement by Achille Brocot, 1870's, 41cm. high.   £770

A Sevres pattern pink-ground porcelain and gilt bronze composite garniture-de-cheminee, circa 1880, the clock 34cm. wide, the vases 26.5cm. high.   £810

Late 19th century gilt metal clock set of Renaissance style, the clock 28in. high, the candelabra 39½in. high.
£2,200

A Mexican onyx and champleve enamel four-glass clock garniture, circa 1900, the clock 20in. high, the urns, 14in. high.   £650

Early 19th century Empire style bronze and marble clock garniture with eight day movement.   £600

A gilt spelter and porcelain composed garniture, the clock 22in. high, circa 1880, the pair of 'Sevres' covered urns, circa 1860, 15½in. high.   £800

CLOCK SETS

A 19th century French ormolu clock garniture, 1ft.1½in. high, together with matching pair of two branch candelabra. £1,000

Late 19th century three-piece onyx and ormolu clock garniture, France, clock 15¼in. high. £470

A French 19th century brass, enamel and porcelain mounted clock garniture, signed Lefranc, 1ft.3in. high, together with a pair of side urns. £1,650

A 19th century French ormolu clock set, 20in. high. £1,400

Gilt bronze and porcelain clock garniture, clock 22½in. high, circa 1880. £860

A French gilt brass clock garniture, the two train movement with Brocot type suspension, signed Rollin a Paris, 21in. high. £1,270

CLOCK SETS

A gilt bronze and white marble clock garniture, dial signed Gille l'Aine a Paris, clock 15in. high, circa 1890.
£485

A gilt bronze onyx and champleve enamel clock garniture, the clock 13in. high, circa 1900.   £495

An Empire ormolu mounted bronzed mantel clock with a seated figure of Ceres, and a pair of urn-shaped cassolettes, 41cm. high.
£1,782

Late 19th century French black marble and bronze clock garniture, height of clock 21in., height of statues 18½in.   £655

A French gilt brass clock garniture , the movement with Brocot type suspension, 14½in. high.   £500

A 19th century French porcelain and gilt metal garniture de cheminee, the clock with glass dome and stand, 44cm. high.   £350

CLOCK SETS

French three-piece ormolu and champleve
enamel clock garniture, movement marked
'A. & N.', circa 1880, clock 16¾in. high,
candelabra 15in. high.   £1,100

A gilt bronze and porcelain clock garniture,
dial signed Connell, clock 14½in. high, circa
1880.   £1,320

Louis XVI style three-piece gilt bronze
and Sevres jewelled porcelain annular
clock set.   £7,500

An ormolu mounted Imari porcelain
clock vase garniture, the circular enamel face indistinctly signed, 20in.
high.   £1,620

A gilt metal and cloisonne enamel clock
set in the Gothic style, the dial signed
W. Angus Paris, 17 Lord Street, Liverpool, 20½in. high, the candelabra 17¼in.
high.   £1,300

A champleve enamel Mexican onyx and gilt
metal garniture, circa 1900, the clock 13½in.
high, the pair of urns 11in. high.   £800

CLOCK SETS

Mid 19th century French alabaster and gilt metal clock garniture.   £340

Oriental inspired French 19th century cloisonne enamel clock garniture by Japy Freres.   £2,000

A gilt bronze and champleve enamel clock garniture, the clock 14in. high, the urns 12½in. high.   £880

Mid 19th century French bronze and marble garniture, signed Crouillard, 21in. high.   £400

A 19th century French silver plated three-piece clock garniture, the striking movement by S. Marti & Cie, 16in. high, together with two five-light candelabra, 19in. high.   £450

Gilt bronze and blue porcelain clock garniture, dial signed Festeau Le Jeune a Paris, clock 19¼in. high.   £2,750

CLOCK SETS

Late 19th century three-piece bronze
and champleve enamel clock garniture,
clock 13¼in. high.   £520

A gilt bronze clock garniture, dial
signed Jackman & Son, movement
signed Mougin, 15¾in. high, circa
1880.   £385

An ormolu and porcelain garniture, circa
1870, clock 15½in. high, the pair of candelabra, 14in. high.   £800

Composed gilt-bronze and champleve
enamel clock garniture, late 19th
century,   £650

Louis XVI style gilt bronze and enamel
three-piece clock set.   £3,000

Bleu-celeste 'Sevres' composed clock garniture,
movement by Japy, 1870's.   £550

DESK CLOCKS

A gilt brass timepiece table compendium, with trade label of John Cockburn, Richmond, base 9in. wide. £3,000

A gilt metal desk timepiece in the manner of Thos. Cole, the dial signed Dent, 34 Cockspur St., 6in. high. £495

A gilt-metal desk timepiece, dial signed Hunt & Roskell London, 5in. high, with a velvet lined travelling case. £800

A Viennese silver, enamel and gemset desk clock on oval base with two dolphin supports, 4¼in. high. £540

A silver-gilt and enamel desk timepiece made by Third Artel, St. Petersburg, 1908-17, 11.1cm. high. £2,800

A gilt metal desk timepiece of long duration and in the manner of Thos. Cole, 7½in. high. £1,100

A silver and enamel desk clock by Liberty & Co., Birmingham 1911. £520

Late 19th century circular silver mounted hardstone desk clock by Faberge, St. Petersburg, 12.3cm. £1,140

Late 19th century French champleve and ormolu desk timepiece, 8in. high. £325

LANTERN CLOCKS

Late 17th century lantern clock, the 6¾in. dial signed John Knibb Oxon, 16in. high. **£1,000**

A wing alarm lantern clock, the 7½in. dial with alarm disc, 15in. high. **£2,250**

A 17th century Stuart brass and steel lantern clock, by J. Ebsworth 'in Bethlehem', London, 'fecit', 16in. high. **£875**

An early 18th century brass lantern clock, dial signed Smorthwait in Colchester, 37cm. high. **£1,200**

A brass lantern clock for the Turkish market, signed John Ellis, London, 36cm. high. **£808**

An 18th century Continental brass lantern clock of small size, 27cm. high. **£1,150**

Late 17th century lantern clock in posted frame, 14in. high, restored. **£1,750**

English brass quarter striking lantern clock, 12¾in. high. **£3,500**

A lantern clock with a 6½in. dial engraved with a ring of tulips, 15in. high. **£605**

LANTERN CLOCKS

Late 17th century small alarm lantern timepiece, dial signed Joseph Knibb Londini, 6½in. high.
£3,250

English brass striking lantern clock by Peter Closson, London, 11in. high. £3,000

A brass lantern clock with pendulum verge escapement, signed Stephen Tracy, London, 15in. high. £715

A lantern clock with engraved dial plate, 15in. high. £935

A Japanese gilt brass miniature lantern clock, 5¾in. high. £1,188

A brass lantern clock by Edward Clement, circa 1791, with single hand, (no pendulum or weight), 13¼in. high. £894

A brass lantern clock, signed Chr. Gould, Londoni Fecit., late 17th century, 15in. high. £2,273

Wing alarm lantern clock, circa 1700, 15½in. high. £1,500

A brass lantern clock, signed Thomas Knifton in Lothbury, London, 15in. high. £2,530

LANTERN CLOCKS

An English brass lantern
clock with alarm, signed
John Ebsworth, 15¾in.
high.   £2,000

A brass lantern clock,
signed J. Davis Windsor,
15in. high.   £1,500

An Italian brass and iron
lantern clock, probably
circa 1700, 35cm. high.
£3,000

A brass lantern clock with
alarm, unsigned, 17th century,
with restorations, 14½in. high.
£1,688

An early lantern clock,
the 7in. dial signed
Thomas Knifton at the
(crossed keys) Loth-
bury Fecit, 12in. high.
£2,200

An early brass lantern clock,
signed on the fret, Richard
Beck, near Ye French Church,
Londini, mid-17th century,
17½in. high.   £2,684

A brass lantern clock, dial
signed Lawrence Debnam in
Froome, 34cm. high. £1,000

A Georgian brass lantern
clock, made for the Turkish
market, signed Jno. Parks,
London, 1ft.2½in. high.
£600

A late 17th century brass
lantern clock, the dial
signed Edward Stanton,
London, 39cm. high.
£1,300

LANTERN CLOCKS

Midlands Clockmaking, a small and rare alarm lantern timepiece, 8½in. high.   £5,000

A Japanese striking lantern clock with alarm, 15in. high.   £2,420

An alarm lantern clock, the 6¼in. dial signed Robert Cosbey, 15in. high.   £2,750

A brass lantern clock, the dial with brass chapter signed Wilmshurst, Odiham, 1ft.3in. high, together with an oak wall bracket.   £1,050

A French brass lantern clock, the circular chased dial with enamel numerals, 41cm. high.   £600

A late 17th/early 18th century brass lantern clock, 38cm. tall, complete with 18th century oak wall bracket.   £1,055

An English brass lantern clock, signed Tho. Power Weallingborow, 15¼in. high.   £1,800

A George II small brass lantern clock with silent escapement, chapter ring signed John Fletcher, 9in. high.   £990

Late 17th century lantern clock, 5¾in. dial signed Henry Jones in ye Temple, 15½in. high.   £1,600

LANTERN CLOCKS

Brass lantern clock, by
Smorthwait, Colchester,
circa 1680, 12½in. high.
£1,500

A Japanese double foliot
brass lantern clock with
alarm, 31½in. high.
£4,000

An English brass lantern
clock, dial plate engraved
with flowerheads, 13½in.
high. £1,250

A brass lantern clock, 39.5cm.
high (probably 17th century).
£1,900

Early 19th century alarm
clock with silvered square
dial, inscribed Samuel
Taylor. £125

A late Stuart brass quarter
chiming carillon lantern
clock, dial signed Edw.
Hemins of Bister, 15in. high.
£3,850

An Edwardian lantern clock
in the 17th century taste,
London, 1902, 6½in. high.
£748

A George I bracket timepiece
movement, backplate signed
L. Bradley, London, dial 6in.
x 8¼in. £800

A brass lantern clock, circa
1880, the dial with leaf-en-
graved central reserve signed
Goldsmiths & Silversmiths
Co., London, 16½in. high.
£748

LANTERN CLOCKS

A small alarm lantern timepiece, dial signed Jno. Rolyat London, 8¾in. high.   £1,250

Early 18th century lantern clock in brass case, by Wm. Kipling, London, 36cm. high.   £1,750

A late Stuart brass minia-ture lantern clock, dial signed Thomas Knifton, 8¾in. high.   £2,750

A N. European striking lantern clock, dated 1672, 8in. high.   £1,870

A Georgian brass miniature lantern clock made for the Turkish market, signed Robt. Ward, London, 5½in. high.   £1,300

A 19th century Japanese lantern clock with red enamel dial, 28cm. high.   £2,100

18th century brass lantern clock by William Wood, Nailsworth.   £1,400

A silver and gilt inlaid strik-ing Japanese lantern clock, 19th century, 250mm. high.   £2,200

Lantern clock, dial signed Nicholas Coxeter, London, circa 1680, 16½in. high.   £2,000

LANTERN CLOCKS

A Charles II brass lantern clock by Thomas Knifton in Lothbury, 15½in. high.
£2,250

A Japanese brass lantern clock, the posted frame 30-hour iron movement with double foliot verge escapement, 11½in. high.
£1,404

A lantern clock, the movement with tic-tac escapement, 15½in. high.
£950

A lantern clock, the broad chapter ring signed Thatcher Cranbrook, 13½in. high.
· £1,540

Mid 18th century brass lantern clock for the Turkish market, signed Isaac Rogers, London, 14in. high.   £652

An English lantern clock, dial signed Nicholas Coxeter, 14½in. high.   £3,850

A small early 17th century brass lantern clock with alarm, 17cm. high.
£2,250

A wing lantern clock, the 6in. dial signed John Ebsworth at ye (sign of the crossed keys) in Lothbury Londini Fecit, 15½in. high, with a wood bracket.   £2,200

A quarter-striking lantern clock, the 7½in. dial signed Marcos Peres London, 18in. high.   £3,250

LONGCASE CLOCKS

A late 18th century longcase clock by C. Horwood of Bristol, 235cm. high. **£1,800**

An 18th century longcase clock, dial signed by John Allen, 79in. high. **£1,000**

Early 19th century longcase clock, the eight-day movement by J. Evans, 7ft. high. **£820**

An 18th century longcase clock, inscribed JN Greaves, Newcastle, 89in. high. **£1,700**

An L. & J. G. Stickley tall case clock, signed with red handcraft decal, circa 1908, 81in. high. **£8,928**

An Edwardian painted satinwood longcase clock, the chapter ring signed Wm. Eastwood, 8ft.2in. high. **£1,945**

An Arts & Crafts oak tallcase clock, by the Colonial Mfg. Co., Zeeland, Michigan, circa 1914, 84in. high. **£1,081**

A late 17th century longcase clock, by R. Seignior, London, 6ft.8in. high. **£3,800**

LONGCASE CLOCKS

A longcase clock with eight-day movement by D. Jones, 7ft.2in. high. £520

A 1930's longcase clock, movement engraved 'Johnston Crawford Production No. 1', 176.5cm. high. £990

An ormolu mounted amaranth and tulipwood longcase regulator clock, dial signed Leroy a Paris, 88in. high. £5,616

A Federal maple tall case clock, by Silas Hoadley, circa 1820, 81in. high. £1,125

Westminster chime grandmother clock, no pendulum, 1920. £150

Art Nouveau mahogany tall case clock, late 19th century, by Gerr Suss, Hamburg, 96½in. high. £930

An Austrian beechwood longcase clock painted to simulate mahogany, circa 1900, 207.9cm. high. £540

A late 18th century Sheraton-style balloon longcase clock with year movement, 7ft. high. £3,600

LONGCASE CLOCKS

A boulle month calendar longcase clock, dial signed Daniel Quare, 7ft. 5in. high.
£20,900

Early 19th century longcase clock with eight-day movement, 82in. high.
£660

A Charles II longcase clock, the 10¼in. dial signed Tho. Tompion, 6ft.11in. high.
£12,000

A tallcase clock, dial signed S. Brenneiser, Penn., circa 1810.£3,793

Federal birch inlaid tall case clock, New England, circa 1780, 90in. high.   £2,133

A Gustav Stickley oak tall case clock, circa 1902-04, 71in. high.   £5,381

A George I longcase clock with eight-day striking movement by T. Martin, London, 85½in. high.
£1,500

An Art Nouveau oak longcase clock, by J. Gruber, 253cm. high.
£2,150

LONGCASE CLOCKS

Federal maple tall case clock by Alex. Willard, Ashby, Massa., circa 1800, 85in. high. £1,940

An olivewood long-case clock, dial signed Joseph Knibb, 6ft.4in. high. £19,800

An ebony veneered month longcase clock, the 10in. dial signed Joseph Knibb, 6ft.7in. high. £20,000

Grandmother long-case clock with Jacobean carving by P. Brown. £400

A longcase clock, by Tomlinson, London, with 8-day bell-striking movement, 76in. high. £1,350

A George III long-case clock, the dial inscribed Jno. Williams, London, 90¾in. high. £1,300

Early 19th century painted and carved tallcase clock, Penn., 98in. high. £10,553

A George III eight-day longcase clock by Wm. Carpenter, 7ft.10in. high. £2,950

LONGCASE CLOCKS
CHERRYWOOD

Federal cherry inlaid tall case clock, New England, circa 1790, 93in. high. £3,500

Early 19th century Country Federal cherry tall case clock, by R. Whiting, Conn., 89in. high. £1,533

A Federal cherry inlaid dwarf timepiece, Mass., circa 1810, 43in. high. £2,256

Chippendale cherry tall case clock by B. Willard, Massa., circa 1773, 88in. high. £12,500

A Federal inlaid cherrywood tall case clock, dial signed by Seth Thomas, Conn., circa 1800, 90in. high. £5,773

A Chippendale cherrywood tall case clock, dial signed by Thos. Harland, Conn., circa 1775, 95in. high. £8,467

A Federal cherrywood tallcase clock, dial signed by Christian Winters, circa 1800, 97in. high. £2,972

A Federal cherrywood tall case clock, circa 1810-30. £1,527

LONGCASE CLOCKS
CHERRYWOOD

A Federal cherry-wood tallcase clock, works signed by B. Willard, Mass., 87in. high.   £4,931

Federal cherry inlaid tall case clock, back of dial inscribed 'Wm. Prescott', circa 1790, 91¾in. high.   £8,391

A Federal cherrywood tallcase clock, dial signed by Samuel Shourds, circa 1770, 89¼in. high.   £1,634

Federal cherry inlaid tall case clock, probably Conn., circa 1790, 93in. high.   £2,666

A Federal cherry in-laid tall case clock, by J. Loring, Mass., circa 1800, 87in. high.   £4,280

Cherry tall case clock, by Jacob Hosteter, 94½in. high.   £1,148

A Federal cherry-wood inlaid tall-case clock, 1800/10, 93½in. high.   £2,275

A Federal cherry inlaid tall case clock, E. New Hampshire, circa 1800, 94in. high.   £4,166

A black lacquered
month going long-
case clock, signed
John Blake, 7ft.
7in. high. £1,400

A scarlet lacquered
longcase clock, sig-
ned Micha. Shields,
Aldgate, 96in. high.
£2,428

A late 17th century
green lacquered
longcase clock,
97in. high. £2,100

A George I green
japanned longcase
clock, signed New-
man Cartwright,
105in. high. £3,780

A green japanned
longcase clock, the
brass dial signed
Jos. Windmills,
London, 8ft.4in.
high. £2,160

A mid Georgian
black japanned
longcase Act of
Parliament clock,
31in. dial signed
Will. Threlkeld,
London, 6ft.10in.
high. £1,540

A George II green
japanned chiming
longcase clock, the
dial signed John
Taylor London, 8ft.
3in. high. £2,592

A George II green and
chinoiserie lacquered
longcase clock, by
Wm. Lambert, London
7ft.2in. high. £950

LONGCASE CLOCKS
LACQUERED

18th century green and gold lacquered longcase clock in chinoiserie style, 99in. high. £1,750

George II green lacquered longcase clock, inscribed George Hallifax, Doncaster. £2,250

A japanned longcase clock, dial signed Chr. Gould London, 5ft.10in. high. £10,000

A George III black and gilt lacquered eight-day striking longcase clock, 8ft. 3in. high. £1,500

A Queen Anne green japanned longcase clock, dial signed Markwick, London, 7ft.11in. high. £2,592

An early George III dark green japanned longcase clock, dial signed Benjamin Baddy, London, 8ft. 7in. high. £13,200

A George II black-japanned month longcase clock, dial signed Fra Robinson, 8ft. high. £2,750

A George III dark green japanned longcase clock, dial signed Thomas A. Deptford, 7ft.6in. high. £1,944

LONGCASE CLOCKS
MAHOGANY

An Edwardian in-
laid mahogany long-
case clock with eight
day movement. £900

Early 19th century
Lancashire maho-
gany longcase clock,
94½in. high. £1,200

Edwardian maho-
gany and marquetry
longcase clock ban-
ded in satinwood,
96in. high. £1,550

A Georgian maho-
gany longcase clock,
the dial with subsi-
diary seconds, 8ft.
high. £3,080

A 19th century maho-
gany longcase clock,
the dial signed Brysons,
Edinburgh, 6ft.6in.
high. £800

A Federal maho-
gany tall case clock,
inscribed O. Hop-
kins, 1756, 95in.
high. £750

A George III figured
mahogany longcase
clock with eight-day
movement, by J.
Lomax of Blackburn,
7ft.4in. high. £980

A Federal eagle
inlaid mahogany
tallcase clock,
works signed by
Effingham Embree,
N.Y., 1790/95,
101in. high. £18,965

LONGCASE CLOCKS
MAHOGANY

A George II 8-day mahogany longcase clock, by Daniel Ray, Manningtree, 88in. high. £2,500

Mid 18th century George III mahogany tall case clock, signed 'Isaac Hewlett, Bristol', 93.1/8in. high. £3,589

A George III Scottish longcase clock in mahogany and veneered case. £530

A Chippendale mahogany tall case clock, works by Thos. Stretch, Phila., circa 1750-65, 92½in. high. £10,769

A Federal inlaid mahogany tallcase clock, dial signed by Aaron Willard, circa 1805-10, 94½in. high. £10,404

An 18th century mahogany longcase clock, by Charles Haley. £1,350

A Chippendale mahogany tallcase clock, dial signed by Joseph and John Hollingshead, circa 1780, 98in. high. £8,174

Federal inlaid mahogany tall clock, by E. Embree, circa 1790, 94½in. high. £9,722

LONGCASE CLOCKS
MAHOGANY

A George II mahogany Yorkshire longcase clock, by Thos. Crofts, Halton, 94in. high. £2,400

A Hepplewhite mahogany inlaid tall case clock, by Wm. Bancroft, Scarborough, circa 1810, 98in. high. £2,100

A late Georgian mahogany longcase clock, dial signed Robert Martin, Glasgow, 6ft. 11in. high. £750

A longcase clock by Edward Hurst, painted dial with cottage scene in inlaid mahogany case, 85in. high. £600

A Federal inlaid mahogany tallcase clock, dial signed by Aaron Willard, 1805-10, 88½in. high. £16,349

A Federal inlaid mahogany tallcase clock, dial signed Alex. J. Willard, early 19th century, 86¾in. high. £2,378

A George III mahogany longcase clock, signed G. Forster, Sittingbourne, 7ft. 5in. high. £1,800

A Georgian mahogany longcase clock, signed on a cartouche John Hart, Yarmouth, 7ft.6in. high. £2,000

LONGCASE CLOCKS
MAHOGANY

George III mahogany longcase clock with swan-neck pediment, 7ft.10in. high. £620

A Chippendale mahogany tall case clock, dial signed by Thos. Wagstaffe, London, case Phila., 1760-90, 87¾in. high. £13,064

A George III style mahogany longcase clock, dial plate signed Henry Jarman, London, 7ft.10½in. high. £2,420

An Edwardian inlaid mahogany longcase clock with eight-day movement. £1,500

A 19th century mahogany longcase clock, the dial signed Barraud, Cornhill, London, 1.98m. high. £580

A Federal inlaid mahogany tall case clock, dial signed by Wm. Cummens, Mass., circa 1800, 96in. high. £11,546

A George III Lancashire mahogany longcase clock, signed H. Fisher, Preston, 7ft.5in. high. £1,980

A George III mahogany longcase clock, the silvered chapter ring signed Rich. Penny, London, 2.08m. high. £1,300

LONGCASE CLOCKS
MAHOGANY

A longcase clock in mahogany, inscribed James Wilson, Belfast, 83in. high. £800

19th century miniature mahogany longcase clock by J. Carter, Warrington, 5ft. high. £1,500

George III inlaid mahogany chiming longcase clock with eagle finial, 7ft. 7in. high. £2,000

A George III mahogany longcase clock, the 12in. dial signed J. Wainwright, Northampton. £1,750

A George III mahogany longcase clock, the 13in. brass dial signed Samuel Young, Bonebury, 7ft.9in. high. £3,000

An 18th century walnut and mahogany longcase clock by Bronne, Liverpool. £800

A Georgian mahogany longcase clock, the dial inscribed J. Leroux, Charing Cross, 86in. high. £2,106

A Georgian mahogany longcase clock, signed Williams, Preston, 7ft. 6½in. high. £2,600

LONGCASE CLOCKS
MAHOGANY

A late Georgian
mahogany long-
case clock, dial
signed Hughes,
6ft.10in. high.
£1,500

Early 19th century
mahogany longcase
clock, movement
striking on a bell,
82½in. high. £1,200

George III maho-
gany longcase clock,
dial signed Robert
Allam, London. 8ft.
2in. high.   £2,000

American Federal
inlaid mahogany
tall case clock,
circa 1800, 93¼in.
high.   £6,965

A Georgian maho-
gany quarter chim-
ing longcase clock,
the dial signed Wm.
Dutton, London,
2.09m. high.£6,800

A Georgian maho-
gany quarter chiming
longcase clock, the
12in. dial signed Wm.
Haughton, London,
2.46m. high. £4,000

A 19th century maho-
gany longcase clock,
signed Simmons,
Coleman St., 2.01m.
high   £1,700

A Georgian maho-
gany longcase clock,
the 12in. dial signed
Will. Phelps, Putney,
2.28m. high. £2,900

LONGCASE CLOCKS
MAHOGANY

Early 19th century mahogany inlaid and crossbanded longcase clock by Fisher, circa 1800, 90in. high. £700

Mahogany longcase clock, signed MacKinlay Edinburgh, 6ft.4½in. high. £800

An early George III mahogany eight-day striking longcase clock, inscribed Benjamin Sidey, London, 6ft.10in. high. £1,500

An inlaid mahogany longcase clock, signed Peter Walker, London, 7ft.8in. high. £1,870

A 19th century style mahogany longcase clock, 8ft.4in. high. £3,800

A mahogany longcase clock by Nathaniel Brown, Manchester, 95½in. high. £2,650

A George III mahogany eight-day striking longcase clock, 7ft.10in. high. £980

An 18th century mahogany longcase clock, maker John Berry, London, 7ft. high. £2,200

LONGCASE CLOCKS
MAHOGANY

Late 18th century mahogany longcase clock by Jno. Carmichael, Greenock, 81½in. high. £900

A Sheraton period provincial mahogany veneered eight-day striking longcase clock, 8ft.4in. high. £1,200

A Victorian mahogany eight-day striking longcase clock, circa 1850. £575

A mahogany longcase clock with eight-day repeating movement, signed Musgrave, 8ft. 4½in. high. £1,750

A George III mahogany veneered 8-day striking longcase clock, inscribed James Vigne, London, 8ft.2in. high. £3,000

Westminster and Whittington mahogany longcase clock with brass and silver dial. £2,100

A mahogany longcase clock with eight-day movement rack striking, 7ft, 2½in. high. £500

A 19th century chiming longcased clock in 'Jumbo' mahogany case, 7ft. 10in. high. £1,400

LONGCASE CLOCKS
MAHOGANY

An early 19th century mahogany longcase clock, engraved Martin Hall. £540

A late 18th century George III mahogany longcase clock, inscribed Robert Hood, London, 94in. high. £9,460

A mahogany cased three-weight Westminster chime grandfather clock, circa 1900. £600

A George III mahogany longcase clock, the dial signed Chas. Cabrier, 7ft.11in. high. £4,400

A mahogany granddaughter longcase clock with 7in. brass dial, 59½in. high. £1,760

An 18th century mahogany longcase clock, the 12in. brass dial signed Philip Lloyd, Bristol, 2.28m. high. £2,800

An inlaid mahogany three-train quarter chiming longcase clock, dial by D. Barrett, circa 1800. £2,100

A George III mahogany longcase clock, arch inscribed Thos. Conley, Whitby. £700

LONGCASE CLOCKS
MAHOGANY

Federal mahogany inlaid tall case clock, probably New Jersey, circa 1810, 94in. high. £4,920

A Georgian mahogany longcase clock, signed Wm. Webster, London, 91in. high. £1,210

A George III mahogany chiming longcase clock by Eardley Norton, 8ft.1in. high. £3,520

Scottish 19th century mahogany longcase clock by D. Robinson, Airdrie, 7ft. tall. £920

A late George III longcase clock in mahogany case with eight-day three-train movement, 95½in. high. £1,400

A Georgian mahogany musical quarter chiming longcase clock, signed J. Cooke, Cambridge, 8ft.2½in. high. £2,800

A Federal inlaid mahogany tall case clock, dial signed by David Wood, circa 1790, 90in. high. £19,951

A Continental 18th century mahogany longcase clock with 11in. brass dial, 2.62m. high. £1,200

LONGCASE CLOCKS
MAHOGANY

A George III maho-
gany longcase clock,
dial signed Wm.
Farrar, Pontefract,
8ft.2in. high.£1,100

A longcase clock
in mahogany, the
dial inscribed Parke,
90in. high. £1,400

An early 19th cen-
tury Irish mahogany
longcase clock, dial
signed Edwd. Smith,
6ft.6in. high. £1,100

Queen Anne style
mahogany tall case
clock, James Wady,
Rhode Island, circa
1750, 84in. high.
£11,240

The Longstreet Family
Federal inlaid maho-
gany tall case clock,
dial signed by Aaron
Lane, circa 1790,
94in. high.   £27,579

A 19th century
mahogany long-
case clock in the
18th century Gothic
style, 215cm. high.
£1,700

Late 19th century
mahogany quarter
chiming longcase
clock, signed Maple
& Co., London,
2.54m. high.£2,500

A George III maho-
gany longcase clock,
dial signed Joseph
Nardin, London, 6ft.
high.   £3,080

LONGCASE CLOCKS
MAHOGANY

A late Georgian mahogany long-case clock, the brass dial signed Samuel Shepley, Stockport, 8ft. high.   £2,808

An early 19th century mahogany long-case clock with brass dial and eight-day movement. £2,000

A mahogany longcase clock, the brass dial inscribed Maple & Co. Ltd., London, 7ft. 11in. high.   £680

A George II mahogany longcase clock, the dial signed Christo. Goddard, 8ft.5in. high.   £2,860

A George III Scottish mahogany longcase clock, the brass dial signed Jas. Mylne, Montrose, 7ft.3in. high.   £1,540

A Chippendale mahogany tall case clock, dial signed by Joseph Hollingshead, circa 1750, 93½in. high.   £2,694

A George III Lancashire mahogany longcase clock, the dial signed Saml. Collier, Eccles, 8ft. 2in. high. £2,750

An 18th century mahogany longcase clock, signed G. Binch, Manchester, 94in. high. £1,000

LONGCASE CLOCKS
MAHOGANY

18th century Scottish mahogany longcase clock by Alex. Miller, Edinburgh. £1,250

A George III mahogany provincial eight-day striking longcase clock, 8ft. 8in. high. £1,500

An inlaid mahogany longcase clock with eight-day movement, 7ft.11in. high. £1,000

Early 19th century mahogany longcase clock, inlaid with boxwood lines and designs, 90in. high. £700

A 19th century burr walnut and mahogany longcase clock, maker's name John Elliott, London, 7ft.6in. high. £2,100

A Federal mahogany inlaid tall case clock, by Samuel Foster, New Hampshire, 1798, 86in. high. £8,333

A George III mahogany 8-day striking longcase clock, dial inscribed Jno. Morse, 6ft.9in. high. £2,600

An Edwardian mahogany longcase clock of small proportions, signed Ollivant and Botsford. £1,300

LONGCASE CLOCKS
MAHOGANY

Federal mahogany inlaid tall case clock, circa 1790, 98in. high. £2,430

George III mahogany cased longcase clock by John Lloyd of London. £3,600

A Federal mahogany inlaid tall case clock, Mass., circa 1790, 91in. high. £4,375

A Federal mahogany inlaid tall case clock, by Lebbeus Bailey, circa 1815, 91in. high. £10,416

A George III Scottish mahogany longcase clock, dial signed John Peatt Crieff, 6ft. 10in. high. £1,650

A late 18th century Irish eight-day, striking, mahogany longcase clock, 7ft.3in. high. £920

Federal mahogany inlaid tall case clock, by J. Bailey, Mass., circa 1790, 93in. high. £12,587

A mid Georgian mahogany longcase clock, inscribed Andrew Reed, London. £2,200

111

LONGCASE CLOCKS
MAHOGANY

Mahogany longcase clock, dial signed McGibbon, Dumfries, 7ft.2in. high. £1,200

A mahogany longcase clock, signed Andrew Evans, Stockport, 8ft.6in. high. £605

A George III mahogany longcase clock, the dial signed Rich. Winch, Hackney, 2.46m. high. £1,800

A William IV mahogany veneered regulator clock, 6ft.3in. high. £1,800

A George III Salisbury mahogany veneered 8-day longcase clock, the dial inscribed Edw. Marsh, 7ft.8in. high. £1,600

A mahogany cased reproduction long-cased clock. £1,650

An early George III period mahogany longcase clock, inscribed Philp, 7ft.8½in. high. £2,000

A late 18th century inlaid mahogany longcase clock, inscribed Wenham, Deerham, 231cm. high. £1,700

LONGCASE CLOCKS
MAHOGANY

A George III maho-
gany longcase clock
with eight-day
movement.
£1,200

Georgian Lanca-
shire-style maho-
gany longcase
clock by Isaac
Young, Liverpool,
7ft.9in. high.
£2,250

Edwardian maho-
gany Sheraton
Revival longcase
clock, inscribed
S. Meredith. £900

An inlaid mahogany
longcase clock, the
13½in. dial signed
Andw. Robertson,
Glasgow, 7ft.3in.
high.   £1,200

A Regency mahogany
longcase clock, the
12in. silvered dial
signed Grant, London,
7ft. high.   £3,800

A small mahogany
longcase clock, dial
signed Johannes
Walley de Bolton
Fecit, 57in. high.
£2,000

A Georgian maho-
gany longcase clock,
the brass dial signed
Thos. Nevitt, 2.14m.
high.   £2,200

Late 19th century
mahogany 8-day rack
striking longcase clock,
by Seddon & Moss.
£3,400

LONGCASE CLOCKS
MARQUETRY

A 17th century walnut marquetry longcase clock, inscribed Thos. Taylor in Holborn, London, 85in. high. £4,950

A gilt metal mounted marquetry longcase clock of Louis XV style, 90in. high. £2,592

Walnut and marquetry longcase clock, signed John Pyke, London, 7ft.5in. high. £4,500

Mid 18th century Dutch floral marquetry longcase clock, signed Lourens Eichelar, 8ft. 5in. high. £4,221

A late 17th century walnut and panel marquetry longcase clock, signed Jos. Buckingham in ye Minories, 2.16m. high. £5,800

A William and Mary walnut and marquetry month going longcase clock, the 11¼in. dial signed Wm. Jourdain, 7ft. 3in. high. £9,180

A Queen Anne longcase clock, movement with five ringed pillars, the dial signed Samuel Stevens London, 6ft. 8in. high. £3,240

A floral marquetry longcase clock, the dial signed Thos. Bradford, 6ft.6in. high. £7,395

LONGCASE CLOCKS
MARQUETRY

Longcase clock with bombe marquetry case, enamel and brass dial. £2,900

A late Stuart Provincial walnut longcase clock, dial signed Thos. Cruttenden in Yorke, 6ft. 11½in. high. £2,420

A Louis XV design longcased clock by Gilbert, Belfast. £3,000

A late Stuart walnut and marquetry longcase clock with 11in. sq. dial, 7ft.0½in. high. £10,450

An early 18th century walnut and floral marquetry longcase clock, signed Cartwright, 7ft.2in. high. £5,400

An early 18th century walnut and panel marquetry longcase clock, signed J. Windmills, London, 7ft.2in. high. £9,000

An arabesque marquetry longcase clock, signed Rich. Colston, London, circa 1710, 7ft.4in. high. £7,059

An early 18th century walnut and panel marquetry longcase clock, the 11in. square brass dial signed Thos. Stubbs, London, 2.10m. high. £11,500

CLOCKS & WATCHES

LONGCASE CLOCKS
MARQUETRY

A marquetry walnut cased grandmother clock, inscribed Jno. Draper, 5ft. 4in. high. £2,650

Late 18th century marquetry long-cased clock, with an eight-day movement, made by Jan B. Vryhoff. £2,500

Charles II early marquetry long-case clock, signed Edw. Stanton, London, 6ft.11½in. high. £7,500

A marquetry long-case clock, dial signed Chr. Gould Londini Fecit, 6ft. 9in. high. £7,560

A William III walnut and marquetry long-case clock, the 12in. sq. dial signed John Marshall, 7ft.1in. high. £8,800

A late Stuart walnut and marquetry long-case clock, dial signed Peter Mallett, London, 7ft.6in. high. £7,700

A William III walnut and marquetry long-case clock, the 11in. dial signed Asselin London, 6ft.11in. high. £5,400

A George I Vernis Martin longcase clock, the 12½in. dial signed Wm. Stephens, Godalming, 7ft. high. £2,160

LONGCASE CLOCKS
MARQUETRY

Olivewood marquetry longcase clock, signed S. Moore, Tewkesbury, 6ft. 4in. high. £6,600

A floral and bird marquetry long-cased clock by Christophe Gould. £8,500

A Dutch walnut marquetry longcase clock, the 11in. dial signed Joans. Klock Amsterdam, 8ft.2in. high. £3,250

A walnut and mar-quetry longcase clock, dial signed John Davis Wind-sor, 6ft.10in. high. £2,500

A late Stuart walnut and marquetry long-case clock, the 10¾in. square dial signed Fromanteel, 7ft. 11½in. high. £14,300

A Queen Anne wal-nut and marquetry longcase clock, sig-ned Fra. Dorrell, London, 93in. high. £1,800

Thirty-hour alarm longcase clock, dial by Wm. Kipling, in a walnut marquetry case in Dutch style. £1,500

A marquetry long-case clock, signed on the chapter ring Windmills, London, 7ft.1½in. high. £4,400

LONGCASE CLOCKS
MUSICAL

A carved walnut musical clock with ten Symphonion metal discs, 7ft.5in. high. £4,800

A musical mahogany longcase clock, movement stamped Elliot's patent, circa 1880, 91in. high. £1,500

Early 19th century mahogany organ clock, dial signed Edwd. Wicksteed London, 6ft.5½in. high. £2,200

A Dutch burr walnut musical longcase clock, signed N. Wyland, Amsterdam, mid 18th century, 113in. high. £3,795

A Black Forest organ clock, the 24-key movement with thirty-six wood pipes, eight-air barrel and painted dial, 97in. high. £2,200

A George III mahogany musical longcase clock for the German market, the dial signed Jos. Herring, 8ft.11in. high overall. £8,800

A late 19th century German walnut polyphon musical disc clock. £3,900

A large Regina oak longcase 15½in. disc. musical box clock, with eighty-six discs, 252 cm. high, circa 1900. £3,600

LONGCASE CLOCKS
OAK

A George III oak cased 8-day striking longcase clock, the dial signed J. Marr of Retford. **£670**

A small oak 30-hour striking longcase clock, the 11in. brass dial by Sam Hanley, circa 1750. **£950**

A carved oak longcase clock, with 3 weights, key and winder, circa 1880, 98in. high. **£1,980**

An early 18th century oak longcased clock with brass dial, by J. Rigg. **£1,000**

Mid 17th century oak longcased 8-day clock, maker Wm. Webb, Wellington, 6ft.6in. high. **£800**

An oak longcase clock, the dial signed Creighton B-Mena No. 120, 91in. high. **£550**

Late 18th century oak and brown oak banded eight-day longcase clock, the dial signed R. Street. **£650**

A carved oak longcase clock, signed Edw. Whitehead, Wetherby, 86in. high. **£660**

LONGCASE CLOCKS
OAK

Oak longcase clock
signed Josh. Rudd,
Bradford, 7ft.7in.
high.   £800

Continental oak
longcase clock,
inscribed J. J. L.
Batz., 8ft.5in.
high.   £1,000

Black oak cased
longcase clock
with brass face.
£650

17th century oak
longcase grand-
mother clock with
single hour hand.
£700

Late 18th century
30-hour oak long-
cased clock, maker
John Kent, Mon-
mouth, circa 1790.
£400

An oak longcase
clock, signed J.
Green, Nantwich,
7ft. high. £1,045

Late 18th century oak
and walnut crossbanded
longcase clock, by Thos.
Shaw, Lancaster. 88in.
£500

An oak longcase
clock, signed Thos.
Brown, Birmingham,
6ft.11½in. high.£726

LONGCASE CLOCKS
OAK

19th century oak longcase clock, brass dial signed John Kendal, with carved door, 88in. high. £850

Oak longcase clock, dial signed Danl Catlin, Lynn, with broken arched hood, 7ft.0½in. high. £1,500

Mid 19th century oak longcase clock, inscribed Tempus Fugit, 90in. high. £850

An oak longcase clock, signed Joseph Miles, Shaston, circa 1795, 6ft.11in. high. £1,000

Late 18th century oak and crossbanded longcase clock, by D. Collier, Gatley, 80in. high. £1,320

An 18th century Dutch oak longcase clock, signed De Wancker TotLoo, 98in. high. £770

George III oak and mahogany cross-banded longcase clock, circa 1785, 7ft.4in. high. £775

A carved oak long-case clock, signed Peter Nichols, Newport, 7ft.5½in. high. £506

LONGCASE CLOCKS
OAK

An oak cased grand-father clock with silvered dial, move-ment by Randall, Newbury.   £700

Late 19th century oak longcase clock, 99in. high. £1,100

American Moorish-style carved oak hall clock, circa 1900, 112in. high.   £2,500

Mid 18th century longcase clock with oak case and caddy top.   £720

George III oak long-case clock, by J. Ivory, Dundee, 7ft. 6in. high.   £696

A 19th century eight-day grand-father clock with a brass dial and oak case. £700

An 18th century oak longcase clock with brass and silvered dial, maker J. Barrow, London.   £1,000

A George III oak longcase clock, in-scribed Thornton, Lutterworth. £360

LONGCASE CLOCKS
PINE

A painted pine tall case clock, by Silas Hoadley, Conn., circa 1825, 93½in. high. **£5,357**

A Chippendale pine tall case clock, by B. Bagnall, Boston, 1710-40, 98in. high. **£5,000**

Early 19th century Federal painted tall-case clock, possibly Berks County, Penn., 96in. high. **£1,427**

George III pine tall case clock, circa 1780, 92in. high. **£600**

A Federal pine grain painted tall case clock, by S. Hoadley, Conn., circa 1830, 86in. high. **£10,000**

Country painted pine tall clock, by Simeon Crane, Mass., circa 1810, 86¼in. high. **£3,833**

A pine polychrome decorated tall case clock, Connecticut, circa 1830, 85in. high. **£4,030**

Early 19th century painted pine tall case clock by A. Edwards, Mass., 91in. high. **£700**

LONGCASE CLOCKS
REGULATORS

A figured manogany longcase striking regulator, signed Whistler, 6ft.7in. high. £2,420

A mahogany month regulator, the 12in. silvered dial signed John Arnold London, 6ft.4in. high. £27,500

A Regency mahogany longcase regulator, the 12in. dial signed Grimalde London, 6ft.1in. high. £6,264

A Scottish mahogany regulator, the 10¼in. dial signed Alexander Ferguson Cupar Fife, 4ft.1in. high. £3,190

A 19th century mahogany regulator, by Hepting, Stirling, 75in. high. £640

A mahogany longcase sidereal regulator with break circuit work, signed Wm. Bond & Sons, Boston, circa 1858, 64½in. high. £17,480

A 19th century mahogany regulator, the dial signed James, Saffron Walden, 1.87m. high. £3,000

A 19th century mahogany regulator with 12in. circular painted dial, 2.09m. high. £2,400

LONGCASE CLOCKS
REGULATORS

19th century pollard oak cased regulator clock with glass sides and white enamel face.   £675

A 19th century Vienna walnut regulator longcase clock, 6ft.10in. high.   £1,300

A mahogany longcase regulator clock with 14in. dial, signed P. G. Wilson, Inverness, 6ft. 7½in. high.   £900

A late Louis XVI mahogany month regulator, 6ft.10in. high.   £16,500

A Victorian mahogany longcase regulator, the dial signed P. G. Dodd & Son. 6ft.3in. high.£1,944

A George III mahogany regulator, the 10in. dial signed Holmes, London, 5ft.11½in. high.   £5,500

An American carved walnut longcase regulator, signed Howard & Davis, Makers — Boston, circa 1851, 8ft.0½in. high.£16,886

A mahogany longcase regulator, the Franklin type dial signed Vulliamy Pall Mall London, 5ft.11in. high.   £8,100

LONGCASE CLOCKS
WALNUT

A Georgian walnut longcase clock, signed John Watts, Canterbury, 7ft. high. £900

A walnut longcase clock, signed A. Dunlop, London, 8ft.10in. high. £1,485

An 18th century walnut Dutch striking alarm longcase clock, 9ft.7in. high. £4,500

Country Chippendale walnut tall case clock, by A. Hutchins, circa 1800, 86in. high. £2,162

An 18th century walnut longcase clock, the 11in. square dial signed Jn^O. Wise, London, 2.10m. high. £1,600

Federal walnut tall case clock, possibly Penn., circa 1820, 81in. high. £1,250

An 18th century walnut longcase clock, brass dial signed Hen. Massey, London, 2.46m. high. £1,800

A Chippendale walnut tall case clock, dial signed by Johnson, London, case probably Penn., 1770-90, 92in. high. £1,463

LONGCASE CLOCKS
WALNUT

American Chippendale walnut tall case clock by David Blasdell, 81¼in. high. £1,750

A walnut alarm longcase clock, the 12in. dial signed Thomas Speakman London, 7ft.11in. high. £2,750

A walnut miniature longcase clock in the George III style, 152cm. high. £920

18th century walnut longcase clock by John Seddon Frodsham. £2,250

An 18th century walnut cased clock by Jno. Baylis of Bromyard. £1,600

Walnut tall case clock, New England, circa 1780, 88in. high, back of dial inscribed 'G.R.'. £1,333

A Chippendale walnut tall case clock, dial signed by Thos. Crow, Delaware, circa 1770, 89¼in. high. £4,410

A 17th century walnut month going longcase clock, by John Knibb, Oxford, 2.08m. high. £13,000

LONGCASE CLOCKS
WALNUT

An 18th century walnut longcase clock, by Windmills, London, 7ft.7in. high. £1,250

A walnut longcase clock, the 12in. dial signed Wm. Threlkeld London, 8ft.8in. high. £3,300

A walnut longcase clock with eight-day movement, dial signed John Dorrell, London, 7ft.8in. high. £2,750

A walnut month going equation longcase clock, signed Geo. Graham, London, 240cm. high. £94,328

A George II burr walnut calendar longcase clock, the dial signed George Merttins, Londini, 8ft. high. £4,950

A Pennsylvania Chippendale walnut tall-case clock, the dial signed C. Warner, 91in. high. £2,234

A Dutch walnut longcase clock, dial signed Andris Vermeulent, Amsterdam, 7ft. high. £3,080

An early 18th century walnut longcase clock, signed Dan. Delander, London, 2.54m. high. £3,800

LONGCASE CLOCKS
WALNUT

A George I month-going walnut longcase clock, the chapter ring signed John May, 100in. high. £6,050

George II walnut longcase clock by Gray & Vulliamy, London, 7ft.6in. high. £2,860

A walnut longcase clock, signed W. Donald, Glasgow, 7ft.1½in. high. £880

A George I walnut longcase clock, by Jos. Windmills, London, 7ft.8in. high. £7,480

An 18th century walnut longcase clock, movement by Wm. Clarke, 8ft. high. £2,350

An 18th century walnut month going longcase clock, the dial signed Christophe Gould Londini fecit, 6ft.10in. high. £3,500

A walnut longcase clock, the chapter ring signed Edw. Stanton, London, 6ft.4in. high. £3,456

A Queen Anne walnut longcase clock, the dial signed Jn. Motley London, 7ft.1in. high. £1,728

LONGCASE CLOCKS
WALNUT

A week-going walnut longcase clock, the 12in. square dial signed at the base Geo. Graham, London, 7ft. 8½in. high.   £30,240

A Charles II walnut and parquetry longcase clock, 10in. dial signed C. Gretton, London, 6ft.3in. high.   £6,600

An 18th century burr walnut longcase clock, the dial inscribed Robt. Maisley, London, 7ft. 6in. high.   £3,300

A late Stuart Provincial burr walnut longcase clock, dial signed Tho. Power, 6ft. 6in. high.   £3,240

A late 17th century walnut and panel marquetry longcase clock, the 10in. brass dial signed Bird, London, 6ft.8½in. high.   £11,500

A Georgian walnut and inlaid longcase clock, signed Jon. Sales, Dublin, 8ft. 5½in. high. £2,400

A Pennsylvania Chippendale inlaid walnut tallcase clock, 88in. high.   £2,483

George II figured walnut longcase clock, by J. Marsh, London, 97in. high overall. £2,450

LONGCASE CLOCKS
WALNUT

A Queen Anne walnut year-going longcase clock, by Daniel Quare, London, 7ft.6in. high.   £22,000

A late 17th century walnut longcase clock, by Daniel Quare, London, 6ft.8in. high. £11,000

A Dutch burr-walnut month calendar longcase clock, dial signed Fromanteel & Clarke, 7ft.8in. high.   £4,290

A Charles II walnut month-going longcase clock, dial signed Thos. Tompion, 6ft.4in. high.   £46,200

An Irish inlaid walnut longcase clock, the 13½in. dial signed Tho. Parker Dublin, 7ft.4in. high.   £2,530

An 18th century walnut longcase clock, by Marm'd. Storr.   £2,000

An early 18th century walnut quarter chiming longcase clock, by Claude Du Chesne, London, 8ft.1in. high.   £8,500

A mid Georgian ormolu mounted walnut clock by Jno. Melling, Chester, 88½in. high. £9,180

MANTEL CLOCKS
ART DECO

Metamec electric clock with 'tick' and 'silent' control, £10

A Westminster chime Admiral's hat clock. £20

An ebony and ivory inlaid mantel clock, designed by Josef M. Olbrich, circa 1902. £16,500

An Alfred Dunhill Art Deco marble mantel clock and cigarette case, 23.7cm. high. £605

A silvered bronze mantel clock, by Edgar Brandt, 30.6cm. high. £3,080

Art Deco hardstone and cloisonne enamel desk clock, with 13J Swiss movement, 4.1/8in. high. £640

An Ato Art Deco table clock with a pair of bronze owls perched on top, 41.5cm. high. £495

A gold, rock crystal, onyx and enamel clock by Tiffany & Co. £2,050

A hammered brass and chromed metal mantel clock, probably Wiener Werkstatte, circa 1905/10, 26.5cm. £693

MANTEL CLOCKS
ART DECO

A Marchak & Linzeler Art Deco boudoir clock, circa 1925, 8cm. £1,930

An enamelled Art Deco timepiece, retailed through Fortnum & Mason, London, 23.5cm. wide, when open, with Swiss 8-day movement. £850

A square Nephrite travelling timepiece with gold mounts, by Cartier, circa 1920, 6.7cm.   £1,400

Early 20th century grey marble and glass Art Deco mantel clock, France, 11 in. high.   £215

An Art Deco style circular pink mirror glass electric mantel clock.   £185

Early 19th century French Art Deco mantel clock with white marble pediment.   £325

A P. M. Faure glass clock case on stepped base, circa 1930, 16cm. £145

Art Deco green onyx cased clock flanked by two ivory figures, 14½in. wide.   £1,500

A silvered bronze Art Deco table clock, signed R. Terras, 34.5cm. high.   £990

MANTEL CLOCKS
ART NOUVEAU

Art Nouveau porcelain mantel clock, elongated 'A' shape with green glaze and eight-day time and strike movement. £140

A carved wood Art Nouveau mantel clock, by the Chelsea Clock Co., Boston, circa 1920, 18¼in. high. £500

A decorative Art Nouveau plaster clock case, signed 'Simon', circa 1900, 97.75cm. high. £640

ARTS & CRAFTS

An Arts & Crafts mahogany mantel clock with bevelled glass, circa 1900, 12in. high. £297

An Arts & Crafts square oak mantel clock, by Seth Thomas Clock Co., 20th century, 12½in. high, 10½in. wide. £648

Victorian oak hanging wall clock with pendulum, 1900. £80

CAST IRON

A cast iron front mantel clock, polychrome painted, America, circa 1890, 11¾in. high. £60

A cast iron and mother-of-pearl shelf clock by Terry & Andrews, with painted dial, circa 1855, 15¾in. high. £130

Cast iron mantel clock with painted dial and eight-day time and strike movement, America, circa 1860, 20in. high. £220

MANTEL CLOCKS
DOULTON

The Menagerie, a Doulton stoneware clock case in the form of a circus building, with incised wild animals, circa 1875, 9¾in. high.   £2,200

A small circular Doulton clockcase in buff stoneware with applied rough cast chips, circa 1890, 7¼in. high.   £170

An early architectural Doulton clockcase glazed ochre and blue, with incised blue, green, and purple leaves, o.m., 1875, 14½in. high.   £850

A monumental Doulton clockcase glazed in shades of blue and brown with carved and incised details and applied bead work, c. m., 1879, 15½in. high.   £1,150

The Fables Clock, the stoneware case modelled with the interior of a house and numerous figures and animals, the base inscribed: H. Doulton & Co., Lambeth, and G. Tinworth, circa 1882, 11¼in. high.   £2,500

A Doulton Punch and Judy clockcase, the buff stoneware with a bright blue glaze, c.m.l. & c., circa 1905, 11½in. high.   £750

A Doulton stoneware bracket clockcase by Eliza Simmance, inspired by 18th century models, r.m. & e., circa 1895, 14½in. high.   £950

An architectural Doulton clockcase glazed in dark brown, blue and green, r. m., 1884, 10¼in. high.
£650

A Doulton Lambeth clock case of rectangular section inset with a circular dial, 14in. high.   £500

MANTEL CLOCKS
EBONY

A George III chiming mantel clock with brass dial and ormolu embellishments, 27in. high. £2,700

An early ebony-veneered pendulum clock by A. Fromanteel, 7¾in. high. £46,200

Mid 18th century ebony veneered mantel clock, dial engraved Willm. Addis, London, 26in. high. £1,250

An ebonised Haagse clock, signed, circa 1660, 36.7cm. high. £5,536

A Royal Presentation ormolu mounted ebony grande sonnerie spring clock by Thos. Tompion, London, No. 278, circa 1700, 28in. high. £248,400

An ebonised travelling or mantel timepiece, the 3in. silvered dial signed De La Salle & Christie, 7in. high. £660

French inlaid ebonised mantel clock, signed L'aine a Paris, 22in.high. £350

A 19th century ebonised mantel clock, the dial signed James McCabe, Royal Exchange, London, 1717, 26cm. high. £1,300

A Louis XV-style ebonised and ormolu mounted bracket clock with fusee movement, 3ft.11in. overall. £450

MANTEL CLOCKS
FIGURAL

A gilt bronze mantel
clock by Raingo Freres,
circa 1870, 19¾in. high.
£1,045

A gilt and patinated bronze
mantel clock with silvered
dial, 23in. high, circa 1830.
£440

A 19th century French
ormolu mantel clock
by J. Silvani, 18in.
high.   £1,000

An ormolu and marble
mantel clock, French, 12in.
high, circa 1860.   £825

A Charles X ormolu and
malachite mantel clock, the
dial flanked by the brothers
Horatii taking their oath,
after J-L David, 21½in. wide.
£4,180

A 19th century French
ormolu and bronze mantel
clock, the gilt dial with
enamel numerals, 1ft.10in.
high.   £800

A French mantel clock with
eight-day striking movement,
13in. high.   £300

Mantel clock on D-shaped
marble base, the clock
face surmounted by a
bronzed group of lovers.
£460

A Charles X ormolu mantel
clock with circular dial signed
'Guyerde(?) aine Paris', 12in.
wide.   £660

MANTEL CLOCKS
FIGURAL

An early 19th century ormolu mounted bronze mantel timepiece, signed Geo. Young, London, 12in. high.　£680

Mid 19th century Charles X ormolu mantel clock, with eight-day time and strike, 23¼in. high.　£370

A French mid 19th century mantel clock with eight-day movement stamped Japy Freres, 12in. wide.　£720

19th century French gilt metal mantel clock on rococo plinth.　£500

A Restoration ormolu 'Troubadour' mantel clock with silk-suspended pendulum, 35cm. high.　£813

An Empire bronze and ormolu mantel clock, the enamel dial signed Lemoine a Paris, 24¼in. high.　£1,650

A Louis Philippe ormolu mantel clock, the silvered dial signed A. C. Decauville A Paris, 24½in. high.　£1,320

A Louis Philippe gilt bronze mantel clock with eight-day striking movement and a glass dome, 16½in. high.　£380

A gilt bronze mantel clock, the dial with silvered chapter ring, 18½in. high, circa 1850.　£420

MANTEL CLOCKS
FIGURAL

An Empire ormolu 'Atala and Chactas' mantel clock, 42cm. high. £1,760

A Regency bronze and ormolu mantel clock with enamel dial, 14½in. wide. £2,530

An early 19th century French mantel clock, with eight-day movement, 12 x 14½in. £340

A Charles X ormolu and bronze mantel clock with silvered dial, 16in. high. £990

An Empire ormolu mantel clock, the silk-suspended countwheel striking movement with enamel dial, 19in. wide. £1,620

An Empire ormolu mantel clock with circular enamel dial set within a plinth with Apollo and his lyre, 20½in. high. £990

Late 19th century bronze and marble mantel clock, 23½in. high. £325

A Charles X ormolu mantel clock with enamel dial surmounted by a bust of Aristotle flanked by a cherub, 19½in. high. £990

An eight-day time and strike clock with J. Pradier bronze, 11in. long. £680

MANTEL CLOCKS
FIGURAL

An Empire ormolu mantel clock cast as an organ-grinder, 33cm. high. £555

A bronze and ormolu clock, the dial signed Raingo Freres, Paris, 25in. wide. £1,836

An early 19th century French mantel clock with eight-day movement, 21½ x 24in. £520

A Regency English bronze and gilt bronze mantel timepiece, 30cm. high. £450

A George III giltwood mantel clock, the associated George I watch movement by William Webster, 13in. high. £990

A French Louis XV style bronze and ormolu mantel clock, the enamel dial signed Thuillier A Paris, 1ft.3½in. £1,400

Mid 19th century silvered bronze and ormolu mantel clock, the backplate signed Leroy a Paris , 26½in. high. £715

Goldscheider pottery clock with oxidised metal circular dial, 20in. high. £250

A 19th century French ormolu mantel clock with circular enamel dial, 35cm. high, together with a base. £400

MANTEL CLOCKS
FIGURAL

French bronze mantel
clock, circa 1860, on
scrolled base, 14in. high.
£350

A Regency bronze and gilt
bronze mantel timepiece,
31cm. high.   £990

A gilt bronze and porcelain
mantel clock, the dial with
arabic numerals, 28½in.
high.   £3,410

Mid 19th century ormolu
mantel clock with circular
dial, 17½in. high.   £550

Mid 19th century French
ormolu and marble figural
mantel clock, signed Caran-
das, A Versailles, 18½in.
high.   £390

A Charles X bronze and
ormolu mantel clock with
circular dial surmounted by
Cato amidst the ruins of
Carthage, 17½in. wide.
£1,210

A French gilt metal striking
mantel clock with blue porcelain face, 28in. high.£650

An Empire ormolu mantel
clock, the dial signed F. B.
Adams, London, 17in. high.
£880

An Empire ormolu mantel
clock with enamel dial signed
Leroy Hr. du Roi a Paris,
14½in. high.   £715

MANTEL CLOCKS
FIGURAL

A Charles X ormolu mantel clock with silk-suspended pendulum, 20.5cm. high. £450

A Louis XVI ormolu mantel clock, the dial signed Le Nepveu a Paris, 12in. wide. £756

A late Empire bronze ormolu and griotte marble mantel clock, 17½in. wide. £1,026

A fin de siecle 'bras en l'air' mantel clock with a gilt metal female figure against an enamel background, 17in. high. £2,376

An Empire ormolu mantel clock, the movement signed James McCabe, London 2133, 12½in. high. £1,650

A 19th century French ormolu and bronze mantel clock, the dial with enamel numerals, 58cm. high. £700

A 19th century French Empire style 8-day striking mantel clock, 17in. high. £340

A Sevres pattern gilt bronze mantel clock, the movement by Gasnier a Paris, circa 1875, 41cm. wide. £825

An Empire bronze and gilt-bronze mantel clock, circa 1815, 31½in. high. £990

MANTEL CLOCKS
FIGURAL

Bronze and marble mantel
clock, dial signed C. P. Jhlee,
a Francfort, circa 1860,
43cm. high.   £460

An Empire ormolu mantel
clock, the steel dial signed
Leroy & fils Hrs du roi,
25in. high.   £990

An Empire ormolu negro
clock with silk-suspended
pendulum, 37cm. high.
          £2,250

A 19th century Black
Forest 'clock-vendor' timepiece, circa 1850, 15in.
high.   £1,320

A French Empire ormolu
mantel clock, the move-
ment mounted on a chariot,
44cm. high.   £1,200

A cast iron blinking eye
timepiece, 'Sambo',
America, circa 1860, 16in.
high.   £930

Late 19th century bronze
and ormolu figural mantel
clock, France, 28½in. high.
          £1,455

A bronze and ormolu mantel
clock of Louis XVI design
with horizontal movement
contained in an urn. £3,240

A Charles X ormolu and bronze
mantel clock with silvered dial,
15in. high.   £1,210

MANTEL CLOCKS
FIGURAL

An 18th century elephant mantel clock, signed Vulliamy London, probably French, 19½in. high. **£1,650**

19th century French black marble and Barbedienne gilt bronze mantel clock, signed, 30in. high. **£750**

A Restoration ormolu mantel clock with silk-suspended pendulum, 40cm. high. **£428**

An early 19th century ormolu mantel clock, 1ft.9in. high. **£680**

A Continental spelter mystery timepiece on a rectangular base, 32cm. high. **£380**

A French 19th century bronze ormolu and red marble mantel clock, the enamel dial signed Guibal A Paris, 57cm. high. **£1,500**

A Louis Philippe ormolu, bronze and white marble mantel clock, with enamel circlet dial, 14in. high. **£715**

A French porcelain mounted gilt brass mantel clock, with the trade stamp of Miroy Freres, 14½in. high. **£220**

An early 19th century timepiece inkstand, the movement with engine-turned gilt face by Edward Lock, 19cm. high, 18cm. wide. **£330**

MANTEL CLOCKS
FOUR GLASS

A French brass and enamel four glass clock with singing bird automaton, 30½in. high. £2,916

Ansonia brass mantel clock, dial with Arabic numerals. £400

A French late 19th century champleve, bronze and glass mantel clock, 15½in. high. £839

A 19th century French gilt brass and champleve enamel four glass mantel clock, 25cm. high. £480

A French brass four-glass clock with perpetual calendar, the calendar dial signed Achille Brocot, 13in. high. £2,970

A French champleve enamel four glass clock, the 8-day movement striking on bell, 13in. high. £605

Late 19th century champleve, glass and brass mantel clock, France, 10¾in. high. £550

A glass and ormolu oval four-glass clock with gong strike, the chapter ring signed Franz Wiess & Sohne, Wien, 13in. high. £1,728

Early 20th century green onyx, glass and brass mantel clock, by Ansonia Clock Co., Conn., 11in. high. £230

MANTEL CLOCKS
FOUR GLASS

An oval four-glass lacquered brass 8-day striking mantel clock with enamel dial, 9½in. tall. **£240**

A French four glass and gilt brass mantel clock, the two-train movement with Brocot suspension, 14¼in. high. **£440**

A French four glass and brass mantel clock, the movement with Brocot type escapement, stamped H. P. & Co., 13¾in. high. **£400**

A French four-glass clock, the dial with enamelled swags above a mercury double chamber pendulum, the top and base of onyx, 27cm. high. **£480**

A Victorian satinwood four glass mantel timepiece, dial signed Webster, Queen Victoria Street, London, 17273, 7¾in. high. **£1,728**

A 19th century French brass mantel clock, the enamel dial signed for Payne, Tunbridge Wells, 1ft.8in. high. **£1,250**

INDUSTRIAL

Late 19th century gilt and patinated bronze and marble industrial clock, probably French, 14½in. high. **£1,151**

Mid 19th century red marble and patinated gilt bronze industrial clock, French, 17in. high. **£1,535**

A gilt bronze mantel clock in the form of a pump with white enamel face, 7¼in. high. **£800**

MANTEL CLOCKS
LALIQUE

A Lalique opalescent glass clock, 12.5cm., 1930's.
£420

A Lalique square-shaped clock, Inseparables, the clear and opalescent glass decorated with budgerigars, 11cm. high.
£1,100

A Lalique clear glass clock of flat square form, 'Inseparables', 4¼in. square.
£550

LANCET

An early Victorian maple wood lancet mantel timepiece, the dial with inscription Thos. Cole, London, 10in. high.   £1,320

A Regency mahogany and brass inlaid mantel timepiece, the circular enamel dial signed Scott, Horl^r to H.R.H. The Duke of Kent, 674, 26cm. high.   £480

A small timepiece contained in an amboyna veneered lancet case with brass outline, by Thos. Cole, 10in. high.   £1,250

LIBERTY

A Liberty & Co. 'Tudric' pewter and enamel clock, circa 1905, 20.5cm.
£715

A Liberty & Co. pewter, copper and turquoise enamel clock, marked Tudric 0150, circa 1900, 33cm. high. £594

A Liberty & Co. 'Cymric', copper, mother-of-pearl and lapis clock, Birmingham 1903.   £6,050

MANTEL CLOCKS
LIBERTY

Liberty & Co. 'Tudric' pewter and enamel clock, designed by Archibald Knox, circa 1905, 20.5 cm. high.
£600

A Liberty & Co. Tudric pewter 'Architectural' mantel clock, circa 1920, 7¼in. high.
£520

A Liberty pewter and enamel table clock designed by Archibald Knox, circa 1900, 14.2cm. high. **£1,296**

LIGHTHOUSE

Eddystone lighthouse mahogany and mahogany veneer timepiece, by Simon Willard & Son, 30in. high. **£50,000**

Late 19th century lacquered brass and painted metal lighthouse clock, probably French, 22in. high. **£1,535**

A Federal mahogany veneer lighthouse clock, by Simon Willard, Mass., circa 1825, 27½in. high. **£72,578**

LYRE

An Empire ormolu and bronze mantel clock of lyre shape supported upon seated griffins, 10½in. high.
£935

A 19th century French white marble and ormolu mounted lyre clock, 1ft.4in. high.
£850

A 19th century French ormolu mantel clock, the case in the form of a lyre, 38cm. high, on an oval ebonised stand under a glass shade.
£580

MANTEL CLOCKS
MAHOGANY

An early 19th century mahogany mantel regulator, the 7¼in. silvered dial signed Reid & Auld Edinr., 17in. high. £2,420

A Regency mahogany mantel timepiece signed Weeks Museum, Coventry St., on the enamel dial, 12in. high. £1,026

A 19th century mahogany and brass inlaid mantel clock, the circular painted dial signed Condliff, Liverpool, 35cm.high. £700

A Regency mahogany and brass inlaid mantel timepiece with circular enamel dial (damaged), 9½in. high. £260

A Regency mahogany striking mantel clock, the dial signed Bateman, Great Tower Street, London, 13½in. diam. £1,512

A mahogany mantel clock, by Breguet, 11¼in. high. £4,200

A fine Georgian inlaid mahogany striking mantel clock, the enamel dial signed Arnold, London, 13in. high. £2,052

William IV period mahogany four glass mantel clock, by W. J. Thomas, London, 12½in. high. £620

A George III mahogany mantel timepiece, the dial signed Absolon, London, 10in. high. £500

149

MANTEL CLOCKS
MARBLE

A 19th century French white marble and ormolu mantel clock, 51cm. high. £480

Early 20th century marble base mantel clock, probably French, dial marked Bigelow & Kennard, Boston, 12½in. high. £590

Victorian black marble mantel clock, 1880. £95

An Empire ormolu mounted black and white marble mantel clock, the enamel dial signed 'a Paris', 21in. high. £4,400

A 19th century black slate mantel timepiece, signed Payne, 163 New Bond Street, 22cm. high. £260

Black Faux marble curfew clock by W. Gilbert Clock Co., Conn., circa 1880, 17.1/8in. high. £175

A Louis XVI ormolu mounted marble pendule a cercle tournant, signed Ant. Coliau a Paris, 15½in. high. £3,070

A French Empire gilt bronze mounted black marble mantel clock, 16in. £275

A Regency white marble and gilt bronze mantel timepiece, the gilt dial signed Viner, London, 8in. high. £450

MANTEL CLOCKS
MARBLE

Victorian marble and malachite clock, 1880.   £80

Victorian malachite and
marble clock, 1860. £218

A Louis XVI mantel clock,
circa 1780, 23in. wide.
£3,190

A Louis XVI white marble
and ormolu mounted mantel
clock, the dial signed Hardy
A Paris, 1ft.2in. high. £850

A white marble and ormolu
portico clock, circa 1830,
the white enamel annular
dial signed Leroy a Paris,
19½in. high.   £825

A Louis XVI white marble
and ormolu mantel clock,
the enamel dial inscribed
A Paris, 1ft.10½in. high.
£950

A French Louis XVI style
black marble and ormolu
mounted mantel clock, 1ft.
9in. high.   £950

Victorian pink and black
marble mantel clock, 1860.
£65

An Empire white marble
clock, signed Robin, H. de
l'Empereur, circa 1810,
17¾in. high.   £1,151

MANTEL CLOCKS
METAL

Late 18th century gilt metal and stone-set musical mantel clock for the Chinese market, signed Brockbanks, 19in. high. £27,000

A Victorian lacquered brass mantel clock with French movement by F. Martie, 16in. high, 22in. wide. £420

A French Gothic style mantel clock, circa 1890, 11¾in. high. £375

A 19th century gilt bronze mantel timepiece, the silvered dial signed for Hunt & Roskell, London, 1ft.7¼in. high. £3,000

Champleve and brass mantel clock, France, circa 1900, 8in. high. £635

A gilt metal timepiece, The Plato Clock, circa 1903, 6in. high. £50

Early 17th century South German gilt metal tabernacle clock or turmuhr, 19¼in. high. £10,800

A Charles X ormolu mantel clock with glazed circular dial, 19in. high. £1,045

An early 17th century crucifix clock with detachable base, signed under the countwheel B.R. 1631, 35cm. high. £5,000

MANTEL CLOCKS
METAL

Gilt bronze mantel clock, stamped Wm. Roskell, Paris, circa 1870, 43cm. high.
£570

Unusual brass drum-shaped night watchman's clock by T. Burk, Malta, 10.5cm. diam.
£40

A 19th century cartouche-shaped cast gilt brass case eight-day mantel clock, 12in.
£180

A 19th century French ormolu and enamel mantel clock, the case decorated with polychrome champleve enamel, 24cm. high.
£280

A multi-dial longcase laboratory timepiece, by T. Wright. £1,155

A French 'Rheims' cathedral clock, the movement with Brocot type suspension, 21½in. high.
£1,320

An Empire ormolu mantel clock with glazed dial in tapering plinth case surmounted by an oil lamp, 15in. high.
£1,760

A Regency ormolu mantel clock, the dial in drum-shaped case, 9½in. wide.
£918

A gilt metal mantel clock with a 3¾in. enamel dial signed Grimalde & Johnson, Strand London, 10in. high.
£750

MANTEL CLOCKS
METAL

Early 18th century chased and gilt brass night clock, signed B. Blaser in Bern, 335mm. high.   £3,503

A 19th century French ormolu and champleve enamel mantel clock, the gilt dial signed for Howell & James, 43cm. high.   £600

A George III ormolu mantel clock for the Oriental market, the dial signed W. Mahr, 19in. high.   £4,400

A 19th century ormolu mantel clock, marketed by Bigelow Kennard & Co., Boston, 24in. high.   £620

An electric mantel timepiece, the movement with enamel dial signed Dollond, London, 44cm. high.   £600

A mid 19th century gilt metal mantel clock in the form of a Gothic tower, 28in. high.   £650

A small Restoration ormolu mantel clock in Louis XV style, the enamel dial signed S. Devaulx Palais Royal 124, 11in. high.   £528

A Continental gilt metal candle alarm with florally engraved plinth case, 5in. high.   £648

An ormolu mantel clock of rococo style, 29in. high, 19½in. wide.   £1,210

MANTEL CLOCKS
METAL

An Empire gilt metal and bronze mantel clock, the base shaped as an orange tub, 17in. high. £3,024

An ormolu mantel clock, the glazed dial signed Gosselin a Paris, 16¾in. high. £770

A Charles X ormolu mantel clock with circular dial and striking movement in a foliate drum case, 19in. high. £880

A George III gilt-metal mantel clock with a 3¼in. dial by Ellicott, 11¾in. high. £1,100

A Japanese gilt brass striking spring clock, the case engraved with stylised flowers and with turned angle columns, 6in. high. £1,296

Mid 19th century Empire style ormolu mantel clock, 22in. high. £400

A 19th century gilt brass mantel timepiece, the enamel dial signed Ecole Horlogerie de Paris, 1ft.6½in. high. £650

Late 19th century French classical Revival brass and glass mantel clock, 14½in. high. £300

A 19th century French ormolu mantel clock, the circular chased dial signed Hy. Marc a Paris, 41cm. high. £800

155

MANTEL CLOCKS
METAL

A mantel clock in gilt metal case decorated with champleve enamelled panels of scarlet, green and blue flowers on a pale blue ground, 2½in. £110

Gilt bronze and champleve mantel clock, movement stamped Maple & Co. Paris, 34cm. high, circa 1880. £550

A mid 19th century French ormolu and Sevres panel mantel clock, under glass dome, 18in. high. £475

Late 19th century silver plated mantel clock, by Leroy & Fils, Paris, 14½in. high. £200

An ormolu mantel clock with enamel dial and drum-shaped case, 12in. wide. £352

A French free standing bronze spelter sculptural clock, with the trade stamp of S. Marti, 48½in. high. £727

19th century metal night clock in the form of a lighthouse, with revolving dial, 21in. high. £300

A French ormolu 8-day mantel clock with porcelain dial, circa 1870, 17in. high, on serpentine shaped base with glass dome. £360

An Empire period ormolu mounted mantel clock, the dial signed Gaston Jolly a Paris, 16in. high. £715

MANTEL CLOCKS
ORMOLU & PORCELAIN

French porcelain moun-
ted gilt bronze mantel
clock by W. H. Tooke,
Paris, 17in. high. £750

A gilt bronze and porce-
lain mantel clock, signed
Leroy Freres a Paris, circa
1879, 10½in. high. £440

A gilt bronze and porce-
lain mantel clock, circa
1870, 16in. high. £640

A 19th century French brass
and porcelain mantel clock,
36cm. high. £1,700

A Louis XVI ormolu moun-
ted Sevres porcelain and
biscuitware mantel clock,
16½in. high. £1,512

A Charles X ormolu and porcelain clock, the movement
signed Leroy , Paris 1102,
16in. high. £770

A 19th century French
ormolu and porcelain
mounted mantel clock,
41cm. high. £520

A 19th century French
ormolu and porcelain mantel
clock, 1ft.3in. high. £720

A 19th century French
ormolu and porcelain
mounted mantel clock, the
dial signed E. W. Streeter,
11in. high. £540

MANTEL CLOCKS
ORMOLU & PORCELAIN

A 19th century French ormolu and porcelain mantel clock, the square dial signed Klaftenburger, London, together with a giltwood base, 46cm. high. £520

A 19th century French ormolu and porcelain mantel clock, the decorated dial signed for Miller & Co., Bristol, 43cm. high. £520

A French gilt brass and jewelled porcelain mounted mantel clock, with the trade stamp of Japy Freres, 16¾in. high. £440

A Paris (Jacob Petit) clockcase and stand of scroll outline, blue JP marks, circa 1835, 37cm. high overall. £825

A 19th century French ormolu and porcelain mantel clock, the enamel dial signed Vieyres & Repignon a Paris, 11in. high. £600

A 19th century French ormolu and porcelain mantel clock, the enamel dial signed Grohe A Paris, 28cm. high. £480

Late 19th century Sevres pattern pink-ground porcelain gilt bronze mounted mantel clock, 34cm. high. £770

A 19th century French ormolu and porcelain mantel clock, the dial signed for F. Armstrong & Bros., Paris, 1ft.6½in. high. £520

A French ormolu and Sevres style panel clock, signed on the dial Lagarde A Paris, 49cm. high. £2,600

MANTEL CLOCKS
PORCELAIN

A Paris (Jacob Petit) blue-ground clockcase and stand, the movement by Hrr. Marc a Paris, circa 1835, 34cm. high. **£528**

A Louis XVI ormolu and terracotta mantel clock, the dial signed Sotiau A Paris, with figures of Minerva and attendants, 18in. wide. **£2,750**

Ansonia porcelain mantel clock with Roman numerals. **£185**

Late 19th century Dresden clock group, 66.5cm. high. **£770**

A Meissen clockcase of shaped outline, the movement with circular dial, blue crossed swords mark, circa 1880, 31cm. high. **£1,540**

A Meissen (Teichert) clock-case, blue Meissen mark, the movement by Lenzkirch, circa 1900, 51cm. high. **£648**

A Meissen clock case of shaped outline, circa 1880, the eight-day striking movement with enamel dial, 41.5cm. high. **£1,080**

A Meissen clockcase with a seated figure of Cupid, blue crossed swords and incised numeral marks, circa 1880, 30cm. high. **£748**

A 19th century French porcelain mantel clock with eight-day striking movement, inscribed Raingo Freres, Paris, 15in. high. **£210**

MANTEL CLOCKS
PILLAR

Late 19th century gilt
bronze pillar clock,
24in. high. £750

A late 19th century French
timepiece with 3½in. plain
glass dial, 9½in. high. £310

An enamel clock globe,
signed Redier a Paris, 1873,
on octagonal onyx base,
20cm. high. £2,655

A German gilt metal monstrance
clock, the reverse with astrolabic
dial, movement late 19th century,
18in. high. £10,450

A Japanese pillar clock, the
hood with glazed lift-up
front, 19¾in. high. £572

A 19th century French
table clock by Vittoz,
Paris, 27½in. high. £750

PREISS

A Preiss clock surmoun-
ted with bronze and
ivory 'Bat Girl', circa
1930, 39.5cm. high.
£2,420

An Art Deco green onyx
mantel clock with ivory figures carved after a model
by F. Preiss, 25.2cm. high.
£2,500

Kneeling girl with clock, a
bronze and ivory figure cast
after a model by F. Preiss,
54.4cm. high. £8,580

MANTEL CLOCKS
ROSEWOOD

A brass inlaid rosewood
night timepiece, the 4¾in.
dial signed Robt. Groves,
London. £200

Rosewood mantel clock by
by E. Ingraham & Co.,
Connecticut, circa 1862.
£1,230

A 19th century French rosewood floral inlaid classical
shaped 8-day mantel clock,
10in. high. £170

A Victorian rosewood four-
glass mantel clock, the backplate signed French, Royal
Exchange, London, 9½in.
high. £1,650

A 19th century rosewood
cased four-glass mantel clock,
dial signed French, Royal
Exchange, London, 9¼ x
6¼in. £2,050

A Regency rosewood mantel
timepiece, the dial signed
Arnold & Dent, Strand,
London, 10¼in. high. £650

A rosewood mantel
timepiece, signed Birch,
London, 8½in. £600

A 19th century rosewood
four-glass mantel time-
piece, signed Vulliamy
London, 7½in. high.
£3,240

Mid 19th century rosewood
mantel clock with carrying
case, signed James Murray,
Royal Exchange London, 12in.
high. £3,227

MANTEL CLOCKS
SILVER

A South German silver fronted telleruhr, the circular movement signed Matthias Geill, on ebonised stand, 14in. high. £7,020

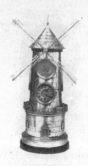

A Fin De Siecle silvered and parcel gilt brass windmill clock, 18½in. high. £880

An Austrian 19th century silver and enamel timepiece, with polychrome champleve dial, 18cm. high. £950

Late 19th century Viennese silver and enamel mantel clock on oval base, 9¾in. high. £3,500

An Austrian silver plated quarter chiming mantel clock, signed Carl Wolfe in Wien, 9½in. high. £420

A 19th century Austrian silver and lapis lazuli decorative mantel timepiece, 22cm. high. £2,600

SWINGING DOLL

Swinging doll timepiece, by Ansonia Clock Co., circa 1890, 12in. high. £465

Swinging doll timepiece, by Ansonia Clock Co., circa 1890, 8in. high. £390

Bobbing doll timepiece, by Ansonia Clock Co., circa 1890, the bisque figure suspended from a spring under movement. £600

MANTEL CLOCKS
TWO PILLAR

A small Louis XVI ormolu-mounted marble temple clock, 16in. high.   £2,750

Late 19th century French Empire crystal and ormolu mantel clock on ebonised base, 20¼in. high.   £600

An early 19th century French mantel clock, by Piolaine, Paris, 17in. high.   £520

An Italian ormolu and cut glass portico mantel clock with chased dial, signed Lacroix a Turin, 16½in. high.   £1,188

An Empire ormolu mantel clock surmounted with a winged putto striking metal on an anvil at a forge, 12½in. wide.   £880

A French Empire striking clock, the movement with outside count wheel, 21in. high.   £550

A George III gilt metal, alabaster and white marble clock, the backplate signed J. Burrows, Goodge Street, London, 19in. high.   £324

A mid 19th century gilt metal striking mantel clock, 20½in. high.   £720

A French 19th century ormolu mantel clock, on an oval rosewood plinth under a glass shade, 1ft.3in. high.   £720

MANTEL CLOCKS
VASE SHAPED

An ormolu mounted por-
phyry tripod vase clock of
Athenienne form, 20in. high.
£6,264

An Empire ormolu man-
tel clock in the form of a
flattened urn with enamel
dial, 42cm. high.   £600

An alabaster and gilt pillar/
vase clock with central milk-
glass dial, 12in. tall, circa 1900.
£225

A George III ormolu mounted
timepiece clock, by James
Tregent, London, in the style
of M. Boulton, 12½in. high.
£7,150

A miniature enamel and gilt
clock, Austria, the urn shape
vase houses a Swiss move-
ment, eight-day clock. £1,200

A mid 19th century
French mantel clock
with eight-day move-
ment, 21in. high.
£2,300

An ormolu mantel clock of
Louis XVI style, the dial
signed Antide-Janvier a
Paris in oval vase-shaped
case, 20in. high.   £825

A lady's boudoir timepiece
in the form of an ormolu
mounted cut glass scent
bottle, signed Jas. Watts,
London, 6½in. high. £770

A Charles X vase-shaped
mantel clock with enamel
dial and swan-neck handles,
13in. high   £825

MANTEL CLOCKS
WALNUT

Walnut cased mantel clock by J. J. & W. Beals, Mass., circa 1840, 13in. high. £300

A walnut cased combined timepiece, barograph, aneroid barometer and thermometer, signed Chadburn & Son, 26¾ x 14in. £462

An American walnut framed mantel clock, circa 1890. £75

A large Victorian chiming mantel clock with brass and silver dial, 28in. high. £900

Late 19th. century walnut cased work's timepiece with punch mechanism. £100

A Regency variegated wood mantel timepiece, signed Davd. Magson, 12¾in. high. £572

A Black Forest trumpeter clock in walnut case, 39in. high. £2,090

Mid 19th century Black Forest carved walnut figural clock, 28¾in. high. £2,027

A late 19th century walnut mantel clock, the dial signed Chas. Frodsham, Clockmaker to the Queen, No. 2057, 30cm. high. £750

MINIATURE LONGCASE CLOCKS

Late 19th century ebonised wood miniature tall clock, by G. Hubbell & Son, 24in. high. £852

A Foley 'Intarsio' earthenware clock case in the form of a miniature longcase clock, circa 1900, 33.8cm. high. £484

Late 18th/early 19th century miniature Continental painted tall clock case, 17in. high. £375

MIRROR CLOCKS

A Federal mahogany mirror clock, by Asa Munger, Auburn, New York, circa 1830, 39in. high. £1,162

An Empire carved mahogany and veneer mirror clock, by Hotchkiss & Benedict, N.Y., circa 1825, 39in. high. £347

Empire carved mahogany mirror clock by Munger & Benedict, New York, circa 1830, 39½in. high. £1,040

New Hampshire mirror timepiece by James Collins, circa 1825, 8-day brass weight driven movement. £800

Classical Revival mahogany mirror clock by Marsh, Gilbert & Co., Connecticut, circa 1830, 36½in. high. £330

'New Hampshire' mirror clock, signed 'Henry T. Southwick Nov. 25, 1831', 34in. high. £600

MOVEMENTS

A late 17th century brass
eight-day striking longcase
clock movement by George
Graham, London. £3,200

An eight-day striking
and chiming longcase
clock movement in-
scribed John Fletcher.
£200

A fine eight-day longcase
clock movement with four
and eight bell chime, inscribed J. Hallifax, London.
£900

PENDULE D' OFFICIER

An ormolu quarter striking
pendule d'officier with
Turkish chaptered enamel
dial signed Courvoisier et
Compe., 8½in. high.
£1,650

An ormolu pendule
d'officier with grande sonnerie and alarm, 8¼in.
high. £2,750

An 18th/19th century
quarter striking pendule
d'officier with verge
movement, 225mm.
high. £2,700

PICTURE CLOCKS

A musical picture clock with figures on a
river bank with the clock face in church
tower. 29½ x 34½in. overall. £1,210

A clock picture of a harbour scene, the
tower containing the 1in. enamel dial,
23 x 26½in. wide. £825

PILLAR & SCROLL CLOCKS

A Federal mahogany
pillar and scroll clock, by
Seth Thomas, circa 1820,
30in. high.   £763

A Federal mahogany
shelf clock, probably by
Seth Thomas, Conn. 1810-
30, 28in. high.   £370

Federal mahogany and
maple pillar and scroll
clock, Connecticut,
circa 1820, 24¾in. high.
£1,000

A Federal mahogany pillar
and scroll clock, by E. Terry
& Sons, circa 1835, 31in.
high.   £774

Federal mahogany pillar
and scroll clock, by Eli
& Samuel Terry, Conn.,
circa 1825, 28½in. high.
£500

Federal mahogany pillar and
scroll clock, by Ephraim
Downes, Conn., circa 1825,
31in. high.   £524

Federal mahogany pillar and
scroll clock, E. Terry & Sons,
Conn., circa 1825, 31in. high.
£454

Federal mahogany pillar
and scroll clock, by Ephraim
Downs for G. Mitchell, Conn.,
circa 1820, 31in. high.   £566

A Federal mahogany pillar
and scroll clock, by E.
Terry & Sons, Conn., circa
1820, 29in. high.   £937

168

ROLLING BALL CLOCKS

A brass rolling ball clock, signed G. H. Bell, fecit, Winchester, 7½in. wide. £1,250

Rolling ball time-piece by G. M. Bell, Winchester £1,400

A Congreve rolling ball clock with separate silvered dials for hours, minutes and seconds, 14in. high. £5,000

SEDAN CLOCKS

A gilt quarter repeating sedan clock, dial signed Lepine, 5¼in. diam. £300

American giltwood hanging sedan clock, 1820-40, 20½in. high. £620

19th century red japanned wall clock of sedan clock form, with gilt decoration, 16in. diam. £430

An early 19th century French brass octagonal cased portable or hanging clock, the movement signed Du Louier a Rouen. £250

Gilt-metal verge chaise clock, 19th century 104mm. diam. £900

Early 19th century French sedan chair clock, 8in. diam. £500

SHELF CLOCKS

A Federal inlaid mahogany
shelf clock, by David Wood,
Mass., circa 1800, 33¾in.
high.   £38,732

Round Gothic shelf clock,
probably by Brewster &
Ingraham, circa 1845,
20in. high.   £400

A Federal mahogany shelf
clock, by Reuben Tower,
Massa., 1836, 34½in. high.
                          £5,725

An Empire mahogany and
mahogany veneer shelf clock,
by Hotchkiss & Benedict,
N.Y., circa 1830, 38in. high.
                          £790

An Empire mahogany shelf
clock, bearing partial label of
Forestville Mfg. Co., circa
1830, 32in. high.   £209

Empire triple decker
shelf clock, by Birge,
Mallory & Co., circa 1840,
36in. high.   £380

Victorian 'ginger bread'
framed shelf clock with an
Ansonia Clock Co. striking
movement.   £68

A rosewood shelf clock, attributed to Atkins Clock Mfg.
Co., Conn., circa 1855, 18¾in.
high.   £1,030

Federal mahogany and
tiger maple shelf time-
piece, by Aaron Willard,
Boston, circa 1815,
35½in. high.   £9,300

SHELF CLOCKS

A Federal inlaid maho-
gany shelf clock by
A. Willard, Boston, circa
1798-1815, 35½in. high.
£6,233

Double steeple mahogany
wagon spring shelf clock,
by Birge & Fuller, Conn.,
circa 1846, 26in. high.
£1,120

Empire mahogany hollow
column clock, Connecti-
cut, circa 1835, 31in.
high.   £240

A carved mahogany shelf
clock, by Marsh, Gilbert
& Co., Conn., circa 1825,
37in. high.   £580

Federal mahogany shelf
clock, by Aaron Willard,
Mass., circa 1825, 34in.
high.   £5,244

Empire mahogany carved
shelf clock, by Eli Terry
& Son, Conn., circa 1825,
31in. high.   £666

An Empire carved mahogany
shelf clock, by Riley Whiting,
Conn., circa 1825, 29½in.
high.   £250

A Federal mahogany inlaid
shelf timepiece, by A. Whit-
combe, Massa., circa 1790,
13½in. high.   £13,740

An Empire carved maho-
gany shelf clock, by M.
Leavenworth & Son, Conn.,
30in. high.   £1,145

SKELETON CLOCKS

19th century skeleton
clock, on stepped
base.   £750

A skeleton clock of York
Minster type, with a
glass dome, 23in. high.
                    £1,500

Early skeleton clock with
fusee movement, under
glass dome.   £275

An iron weight-driven
alarm chamber timepiece
in the Gothic manner,
22in. high.   £1,760

A Eureka electric striking clock,
signed Eureka Clock Co. Ltd.,
London, 11in. high overall.
                    £1,760

A brass Eureka mantel timepiece, the enamel dial inscribed S. Fisher Ltd., 1ft.1in.
high, under a damaged glass
shade.   £400

A 19th century pierced brass
repeating cathedral skeleton
clock with glass dome. £950

Late 19th century brass
skeleton clock with fusee
movement, England, 16in.
high.   £500

A small skeleton timepiece,
on mahogany base with
glass dome, 11in. high.
                    £715

SKELETON CLOCKS

A skeleton clock of Lichfield Cathedral type, dated 1851, 17½in. high. £770

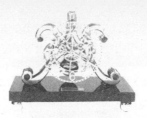

A Victorian brass 'Strutt' epicyclic skeleton clock, slate base with plaque signed W. Wigston, Derby, No. 51, W. Strutt Esq. Inv., 10¼in. high. £2,860

19th century striking brass skeleton clock with fusee movement, 16½in. high. £275

A 19th century brass skeleton clock of Gothic design, 12in. high. £375

A quarter chiming skeleton clock, the pierced plates of open and angular design, 21in. high. £2,160

A skeleton clock, the silvered dial signed John Carr Swaffham, 9½in. high. £770

A Victorian brass skeleton clock, 12½in. high, with glass dome. £2,420

A Brighton Pavilion skeleton clock with pierced silvered chapter ring, 16½in. high. £2,530

A 19th century brass skeleton clock, on an oval rosewood base, under a glass shade, 1 ft. 11in. high. £1,700

SKELETON CLOCKS

Early 19th century French skeleton timepiece in foliate gilt surround, 14in. high. £1,265

A skeleton clock with an annular silvered chapter ring and pierced hands, the plaque signed Litherland Davies & Co., 17½in. high. £2,640

Orrery clock under glass dome, Limited Edition numbered 259. £250

A Victorian brass chiming skeleton clock on rosewood base with replacement perspex gabled cover, 24in. high. £2,484

15in. brass skeleton timepiece with strike and chain drive, under dome. £230

Mid 19th century brass skeleton timepiece with fretted silvered dial, 16in. high. £300

A Victorian brass skeleton chiming clock of York Minster type, 27½in. high overall. £3,240

A late Victorian novelty clock in the form of a ship, the pendulum surmounted by a figure of a helmsman at the wheel. £720

A 19th century English brass skeleton clock with steel chapter ring, on white marble oval base and under a glass dome, 18in. high. £700

SKELETON CLOCKS

An early Victorian brass striking skeleton clock of Lichfield Cathedral type, 16½in. high. £600

A 19th century skeleton timepiece, the glass dial with visible motion work, 7½in. high. £520

Chiming skeleton clock of York Minster type, by Riddels Ltd., Belfast, 25in. high. £3,300

A brass skeleton timepiece with spring detent escapement on oval white marble base, 17in. high excluding dome. £1,535

An early Victorian brass striking skeleton clock, signed Harrison Darlington, 12¼in. high, excluding dome. £1,320

A brass skeleton timepiece with coup perdu escapement, on oval base with two plinths, 14in. high. £1,151

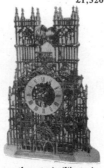

An English brass striking skeleton clock of York Minster type, on wood base with glass dome, 59cm. high. £1,313

A brass three-train 'Westminster Abbey' skeleton clock, striking on gong and nest of eight bells having mercury pendulum, 24in. high. £4,200

A brass chiming skeleton clock, on oval oak base with glass dome, English, circa 1900, 24in. high including dome. £3,837

STREET SIGNS

Hudson's Soap sign,
18in. high, circa 1900.
£60

'Ingersoll Watches'
enamel sign, circa 1900.
£100

Hudson's Soap sign,
18in. high, circa 1900.
£60

STRUT CLOCKS

A gilt metal calendar strut
clock, the backplate stamped Thos. Cole, London,
5½in. high.   £1,836

A gilt metal strut clock attributed to Thos. Cole, 5¼in.
high.   £990

A gilt brass calendar strut
clock attributed to Thos.
Cole, London, the back-
plate signed Hunt & Ros-
kell, London, 5½in. high.
£1,430

An ormolu strut clock, in the
manner of Thos. Cole, the
silvered dial signed Hunt &
Roskell, London, 5½in. high.
£810

A Victorian strut clock with
enamel dial signed Baudin
Freres, Geneve, 8in. high.
£550

A gilt-metal strut clock,
the silvered dial signed
Hunt & Roskell London,
5½in. high, with a velvet
lined travelling case. £850

TABLE CLOCKS

An enamelled silver grande sonnerie world time table clock, signed Patek Philippe & Co., Geneve, 7½in. diam. £23,531

An hexagonal brass striking table clock, circa 1730, diam. of chapter ring 88mm. £2,090

An early English alarm 'table' clock, the movement signed Eduardus East, Londini, 3¾in. diam. of dial. £7,020

A 17th century gilt brass table clock, the rectangular case surmounted by a bell, 17cm. high. £2,200

Mid 18th century Turkish hexagonal brass cased table clock, 150mm. £2,090

Late 19th century enamelled silver gilt Renaissance style table clock, the case by H. Bohm, Vienna, 7½in. high. £806

A German gilt brass square timepiece alarm signed Ang. Metzke Soran, 3¼in. square. £2,268

A mid 17th century French gilt brass table clock with minute hand, calendar and alarm, signed G. Estienne A Caen, 12in. high. £161,333

Early 18th century German gilt brass octagonal table clock, the top plate signed L. Petitot, Berlin, 4¼in. diam. £3,024

TABLE CLOCKS

An early Anglo-Flemish weight driven clock, circa 1600, 19cm. high. £750

A 16th century gilt metal drum clock, 6cm. diam., together with an alarm mechanism of drum form. £1,500

An incomplete gilt-metal 16th century clock case, with later chapter ring and later glazed circular aperture, length of base 200mm. £1,500

A French rosewood regulateur de table, signed Breguet et Fils on the silvered dial, 25¼in. high. £6,451

A German gilt brass octagonal quarter striking table clock, the verge movement signed Christoph Forcker, Breslau, 3¾in. high. £2,160

A 16th century gilt metal table clock, by Hans Gruber, the whole case well engraved, 23cm. high. £4,400

A 17th century South German gilt metal quarter striking table clock, the movement signed J. O. H., for Johann Ott. Halaicher, 13.5cm. sq. £2,420

A Germanic Renaissance gilt metal table clock case, the backplate signed Johannes Benner Aug., the case partly 16th/17th century, the movement 17th century, 17in. high. £3,204

A mid 16th century South German gilt brass drum clock case, 2¾in. diam. £864

TRAVELLING ALARMS

Smith's alarm clock in chromium plated case. £2

'Looping' Swiss travel alarm clock in red leatherette case. £5

Early 60's Equity made alarm clock with luminous hands and central optical moving design. £6

Switana alarm clock with paper dial. £5

A modern Swiss singing bird box in engine-turned lacquered brass case, surmounted by a French 8-day alarm clock, 6in. high, with travelling case. £1,320

Veglia travelling alarm clock, made in Italy, 1950's. £3

'Ebosa' Swiss travel alarm clock, circa 1960. £7

Lady's travelling handbag Swiss alarm clock. £12

'Darling' Swiss travel alarm clock, circa 1960. £7

TRAVELLING CLOCKS

A rosewood mantel or travelling clock, the 3½in. dial signed Frodsham, 10in. high.
£2,750

An unusual early 19th century French travelling alarm timepiece and lighter inscribed Brevet D'Invention, 3¼in. high. £800

A silver and rosewood travelling or mantel clock, 6¼in. high. £440

Early 19th century mahogany grande sonnerie mantel clock by Dubois & Fils, Jura, 10in. high.
£2,000

A travelling clock in scroll and flower embossed silver case, by Charles James Fox, London, 1899, 3¼in. overall.
£380

A small satinwood mantel timepiece, the dial signed Donaldson, 6¾in. high.
£748

A Swiss travelling clock, the enamel face inscribed 'Goldsmiths and Silversmiths Co. Ltd.', London import marks for 1913, 2½ x 1¼in. wide.
£600

A hardstone and enamel timepiece, unmarked, circa 1900, 16.5 cm. high.
£2,750

Late 19th century Faberge gold mounted and jewelled nephrite miniature timepiece, 5.5cm. £3,300

TRAVELLING CLOCKS

Early 19th century alarm clock, 11½in. high, Jura. £1,250

Dutch gilt travelling clock by Johannes van Ceulen, £2,500

An 18th century German silver clock, 5¾in. high. £2,000

9ct. yellow gold cased boudoir clock, London, 1912, 5.6cm. high. £290

Early 18th century gilt brass quarter striking travelling clock, signed Benedict Firsten Feldr, Fridberg. £5,120

An enamel and hardstone quarter repeating travelling clock, signed E. Mathey, Nocturne, 70mm. high. £1,078

Sterling silver 8-day travelling clock, Swiss movement 'Black Starr & Frost, New York', 4 x 2in. £140

A Galle carved and acid-etched clock, 13cm. high. £2,860

Early 19th century travelling clock by Gordon of London, 9in. high. £1,750

WALL CLOCKS

A 19th century wall clock contained in an oak case, with brass dial, 43in. high. £560

An adapted George III brass mounted mahogany wall clock, the dial signed Mattw. & Willm. Dutton, London, 38in. high. £1,296

A mahogany wall clock, the 12¼in. dial signed Vulliamy London, 24in. high. £1,320

A Georgian mahogany wall timepiece, the 1ft.7in. diam. painted wood dial signed Field, Bath, 3ft.7in. high. £600

A Regency mahogany wall regulator, the movement of two week duration, 65in. high. £3,080

Victorian oak wall clock with pendulum, 1890. £90

Oak observatory wall regulator, dial signed T. Cooke & Sons, London, in glazed case, 4ft. 7in. high. £2,090

A 19th century mahogany wall timepiece, the brass dial signed Mattw. & Thos. Dutton, London, 2ft.2½in. high. £2,500

Highland Railway, a mahogany eight-day wall clock, dial inscribed H. Ry. Ferguson, Inverness, 58in. high. £540

WALL CLOCKS

A mahogany tavern time-piece with five pillar movement, 43½in. £693

A late 17th century walnut wall clock, dial signed John Knibb, 24½in. high. £5,500

19th century Tiffany bronze banjo-shaped wall clock, 38in. high. £3,400

A figured mahogany trunk dial wall timepiece, the 15in. silvered dial signed Charles Fox, 57½in. long. £680

A wall clock in carved mahogany case. £100

A 19th century rosewood and ormolu mounted wall clock and barometer, the dial signed Aubert & Klaftenberger, London, 4ft.2in. high. £3,200

A mid 19th century wall clock contained in a walnut case, all enclosed by a black and gilt painted glass panel door, 40in. high. £480

A 19th century 8-day rosewood and oak cased wall clock with painted metal dial. £125

George III mahogany wall timepiece, dial signed W. Thomas Lincoln, 4ft.11in. high. £1,210

WALL CLOCKS
AMERICAN

Waterbury oak long drop regulator school house clock with hexagonal face, 32¼in. high.   £300

A mahogany wall timepiece, Elnathan Taber, Massa., circa 1825, 34.7/8in. long.
£6,200

A Federal mahogany lyre timepiece, Henry Allen Hinckley, Massa., circa 1825, 38in. high. £1,550

A Federal gilt and eglomise girandole clock, by Lemuel Curtis, Concord, Mass., circa 1816, 46in. high.   £7,980

A cherry wall regulator time-piece, by Seth Thomas Clock Co., Conn., circa 1880, 36in. long.   £419

Late 19th century walnut regulator timepiece, by The E. Howard Watch & Clock Co., Boston, 40in. high.   £625

Rosewood veneer wall regulator, by Seth Thomas, Conn., circa 1860, 31¼in. long.   £380

A walnut regulator wall clock, by E. Howard & Co., Boston, circa 1875, 43in. high.   £2,635

Late 19th century walnut regulator timepiece, by the Chelsea Clock Co., Mass., 35in. high.   £590

WALL CLOCKS
CONTINENTAL

A German zappler wall
clock with thirty-hour
movement, 30cm. high.
£1,800

A German zappler wall
clock, dial signed Johan
Bohm, 30.5cm. high.
£1,250

A Schwartzwald wooden
zappler wall clock, the dial
bearing the date 1740,
36cm. high.   £1,700

An ormolu and bronze
clock with glazed enamel
dial, indistinctly signed
. . . Armentieres, 32½in.
high.   £1,320

A late 17th century Italian
day and night clock, signed
Jean Baptiste Gonnon a
Milan, 20 x 23½in.   £2,530

A musical 19th century German
carved wood wall clock, 6ft.11in.
high.   £6,800

Late 19th century softwood
German wall clock, the white
enamel dial with 8-day movement, 13in. high.   £420

An 18th century Dutch
'Stoelklok', 71cm. high.
£680

A Dutch marquetry 'Koort-
staartklok' with automaton,
19th century, 39in. high.
£1,430

WALL CLOCKS
CONTINENTAL

A German zappler wall
clock, containing a bird-
cage iron movement,
dated 1743, 44cm. high.
£2,000

A German weight-driven
wall clock, circa 1600,
18in. high.   £4,250

German 17th century
gilt-metal clock, back-
plate signed Johann
Michael Brugel, 15in.
high.   £5,000

An Empire musical Staart-
klok with painted dial,
179cm. high.   £10,260

A small Black Forest wall
clock, circa 1850, the 6cm.
enamel dial mounted on a
repousse brass surround,
4¾in. high.   £570

An Austrian Biedermeier
mahogany quarter striking
wall clock, 41½in. high.
£1,650

A Germanic iron chamber
clock, the posted frame
30-hour movement with
fabricated wheels, 22in.
high.   £2,860

A French bracket wall clock,
the white enamelled dial signed
Causard Horloger Du Roy,
Paris, the back plate stamped
Vincenti, Paris.   £2,200

A French electrical wall regulator signed Systeme Campiche
de Metz and Mees Nancy on
the dial.   £864

186

WALL CLOCKS
CONTINENTAL

18th century German zappler wall clock with brass and iron thirty-hour movement.
£750

Unusual late 18th century Black Forest wall clock of wood construction. 13in. high.
£1,500

A German zappler wall clock with thirty-hour movement, 29cm. high.
£600

Early 19th century Friesland wall clock, Holland, 45in. high.
£470

Bassetaille enamelled clock, open blue umbrella incorporating 24ct. gold leaf numerals on dome, 3½in. diam., France, circa 1900.
£315

Late 17th century Swiss clock with shaped rectangular iron dial, 40cm. high.
£1,500

French 18th century wall clock with dual striking, by Basnard.
£240

A French Louis XVI 3-month duration console clock, signed on a porcelain plaque Nicolas Texier a Philippeville, 23½in. high.
£4,180

A Black Forest wall clock, circa 1840, the 11in. moulded wood dial with alarm disc, 15½in. high.
£320

WALL CLOCKS
ROUND FACE

A fine 18th century English dial timepiece with verge escapement, signed William Ward, Bloomsbury.   £1,400

A George III eight-day wall clock, the dial inscribed Gray and Reynolds, Wimborne, 16in. high.   £1,300

A George III brass wall clock, the dial signed Edwd. Pashier, London, 1ft.6½in. high.   £1,400

A George III mahogany wall timepiece, the 12in. silvered dial signed Jefferys, London, 1ft.4½in. high.   £1,200

Early 19th century inlaid mahogany clock with brass bezel and convex 10in. dial.   £420

An 8-day fusee wall clock in mahogany case, the cream painted dial inscribed 'Ganthony'.   £740

A Georgian giltwood wall dial clock, the 14in. enamel dial signed Geo. Yonge, London, 24in. diam.   £1,540

Mid 19th century wall clock in circular mahogany case, the enamel dial inscribed Ed. Russell, Foulsham.   £225

A Georgian mahogany wall dial clock, the dial signed Robt. Mawley London, 13½in. diam.   £970

WALL CLOCKS
VIENNA REGULATORS

A late Biedermeier rosewood Vienna regulator stamped Crot Berlin 302 on the back-plate of the weight driven movement, 39½in. high.
£810

A Vienna walnut regulator wall clock. £300

Mid 19th century walnut and ebonised Vienna wall timepiece. £390

A Continental eight-day mahogany weight driven two-train Vienna regulator, 58in. high. £340

A mahogany Vienna regulator with satin birch line inlay to the glazed case, 19th century, 36½in. high. £1,890

A mid 19th century Biedermeier mahogany Vienna regulator, 40½in. high. £4,860

A large walnut and ebonised single train weight-driven Vienna regulator, with 9.5in. enamel face. £2,000

Victorian Vienna wall clock with pendulum, 1880. £180

A 19th century carved mahogany Vienna wall clock, 4ft.9in. high. £575

WATCHSTANDS

Victorian gilded metal watch stand designed as a mother-of-pearl bird-bath. £60

Late 19th century nickel plated paperweight time-piece, by New Haven Clock Co., 7½in. high.   £100

A mahogany and rosewood watch stand on inverted bun feet, 6½in. high. £100

German porcelain watch holder entitled 'Gravelotte'. £200

A French Napoleonic prisoner-of-war carved bone watchstand, in the form of a classical arch supported by two Roman soldiers, height 8¾in., width 6in.   £300

German porcelain watch-holder 'Unser Fritz'. £200

A gilt metal clock, by Thos. Cole, London, simulating a watchstand in the form of a miniature chiffonier set, 5¼in. high.   £4,104

German porcelain watch-holder 'Sedan'   £175

20th century American ebony and ivory watch-stand, 6¼in. high. £250

WATCHES

Early 19th century gold verge watch with retrograde second hand , probably Swiss, 55mm. diam.   £1,277

French gold and enamel form watch in the shape of a helmet, 25mm. diam.   £3,500

A gold and enamel musical automaton watch with white enamel dial, 57mm. diam., circa 1810.   £15,765

A French gold and enamel verge watch , with wound through enamel dial, 57mm. diam.   £2,916

A yellow metal keyless cylinder fob watch or miniature clock in the form of a Lancashire style longcase clock, 46mm. high.   £594

A Continental gold and enamel quarter repeating watch, the movement with ruby cylinder escapement, 37mm. diam.   £900

An openface pocket watch, the white face inscribed 'Shock proof lever, Swiss made' and depicting a monoplane, 2in. diam.   £55

An 18ct. gold quarter repeating pocket watch, keyless, with white enamel dial plate with black Roman numerals.   £400

An 18ct. gold half hunting cased keyless lever watch, hallmarked Birmingham 1910, 50mm.   £385

WATCHES

A gold hunter-cased keyless lever minute repeating watch, London, 1903, 55mm. diam. £2,500

18ct. gold open-faced keyless lever watch hallmarked 1881, 49mm. diam. £300

A Swiss gold keyless lever watch, 55mm. diam. £1,404

A floral enamel silver gilt centre seconds watch for the Chinese Market, Swiss, mid 19th century, 57mm. diam. £2,016

A 19th century Austrian silver gilt, enamel and rock crystal verge watch, 68mm. across. £2,000

Late 19th century enamelled silver openface lever watch with centre seconds for the Chinese market, 39mm. diam. £565

A French gold quarter repeating musical cylinder watch with plain balance, musical disc and gilt cuvette, 59mm. diam. £2,530

A French gold and gem set verge watch, the case with three-colour decoration set with turquoise and rubies, 42mm. diam. £500

A Continental gold verge watch, the bridge-cock movement with gold dial and serpentine hands, 55mm. diam. £352

WATCHES

Silver centre-seconds
double time lever watch,
circa 1860, 54mm. diam.
£600

18ct. gold Swiss hunter
cased keyless lever minute
repeating chronograph,
circa 1900, 58mm. £2,500

An American 14ct. gold
openface watch, 44mm.
diam. £696

A Continental 14ct. gold
cased keywind pocket watch,
the circular gilt dial with gilt
Roman numerals. £200

A Swiss silver Masonic keyless lever watch, the triangu-
lar case with mother-of-pearl
dial, 60mm. high. £850

A gold quarter-repeating
automaton watch, 55mm.
diam., circa 1820. £3,080

A gold openface chrono-
graph with calendar and
moon phases, Swiss, circa
1885, 50mm. diam.
£1,062

A mid 16th century spheri-
cal gilt metal French watch
case, 52mm. diam. £1,265

An 18ct. gold lever watch,
the gold dial inscribed with
twenty-four hour divisions,
the case marked London
1860, 50mm. diam. £550

WATCHES

An American hunter-cased watch with vari-coloured gold decoration, 52mm. diam. £350

18ct. gold open-faced key-wind watch, hall-marked 1849, 53mm. diam. £350

A Swiss 14ct. gold hunter-cased calendar chronograph, 55mm. diam. £1,750

Mid 19th century Swiss three colour gold, pearl, turquoise and pink stone watch. £550

An 18kt.gold half hunter keyless lever gentleman's pocket watch. £400

A gold openface quarter repeating watch with auto-maton, 18ct. gold case, 56mm. diam. £1,821

A Swiss gold openface musical quarter repeating watch, circa 1820, 56mm. diam. £2,049

An enamelled gold hunter cased watch, Swiss, circa 1910, 52mm. diam. £3,500

A Swiss gilt metal and enamel verge watch, wound through Arabic enamel dial, 54mm. diam. £440

WATCHES

A Swiss gold quarter-repeating keyless lever watch, 51mm. diam.
£691

A Swiss gold hunter cased minute repeating keyless lever perpetual calendar watch, 57mm. diam.
£9,828

A gold musical watch, circa 1820, 57mm. diam.
£1,760

A 19th century Swiss three-colour gold, turquoise and pink stone watch.   £475

Early 19th century gold floral enamel quarter repeating cylinder watch with centre seconds, 65mm. diam.   £56,600

A gun metal double dial calendar watch with white enamel dial, 52mm. diam.
£268

An 18ct. yellow gold Captain's watch, together with chain and key.   £1,300

A Swiss gold and enamel musical automaton verge watch, circa 1820, 60mm. diam.   £12,960

A Swiss gold openface watch, signed with Patent No. 98234, the 18ct. gold case, London, 1925, 51mm. diam.
£571

A gold hunting cased minute repeating keyless lever-perpetual calendar watch, hallmarked 1886, 52mm. diam.   £6,820

A gold hunter cased quarter repeating watch with concealed erotic automaton, Swiss, circa 1890, 50mm. diam.   £3,235

A silver gilt satchel containing a Swiss cylinder movement, inscribed 1876, 28mm. long.   £400

An openface gun metal calendar watch with damascened bar pattern lever movement, 62mm. diam.   £115

A Swiss gold openface skeletonised quarter repeating verge watch with erotic automaton, circa 1820, 56mm. diam.   £4,554

A Swiss gold and enamel hunter cased cylinder watch, the gilt bar movement with engraved gold dial, 36mm. diam.   £700

A small enamelled gold verge watch, Swiss, circa 1800, 30mm. diam.   £200

A Continental gold quarter repeating ruby cylinder watch, 49mm. diam.   £605

Late 19th century 14ct. gold openface calendar watch, Swiss, 50mm. diam.   £345

**WATCHES
NAMED**

Late 19th century gold open faced eight-day lever watch, engraved London and Ryder, 17 New Bond Street, 55mm. diam.   £530

A gold hunter-cased quarter repeating calendar watch, signed L. A. Favre Brandt, Geneve, 53mm. diam.   £1,228

18ct. gold open-faced keywound lever watch by Langford, London, 1877, 49mm. diam.   £500

A repousse gold pair-cased verge watch, signed J. Markham, London, no. 6828, 51mm. diam.   £1,296

A keyless gold openface minute-repeating watch with perpetual retrograde calendar, signed on the case Eugene Lecoultre, 54mm. diam.   £6,050

Late 18th century gilt-metal pair cased striking cylinder chaise watch No. 213 by Marriott of London, 132mm. diam.   £2,420

A French gold and enamel verge watch, the bridge-cock movement signed Le Febure A Paris No. 792, 36mm. diam.   £486

Mid 19th century gold open-face pivoted detent chronometer for the American market, Swiss, the dial signed William F. Ladd, 46mm. diam.   £336

A French gold jump hour cylinder watch, the gold cuvette signed Leroy hger Du Roi Palais Royal No. 114 cof, No. 4780, 42mm. diam.   £1,620

WATCHES
NAMED

Gold half hunter free sprung lever watch by E.J. Loseby, Leicester, 55mm. diam.
£750

A Swiss gold centre seconds quarter-repeating cylinder watch, gold cuvette signed La Croix et Fils a Geneve, 55mm. diam. £1,500

Dent 18ct. yellow gold cased open-faced pocket watch, London, 1898, signed. £600

A gold openface lever watch, signed Paul Ditisheim, La Chaux-De-Fonds, 56mm. diam. £1,479

A verge watch, the movement signed Daniel Delander, London, 334, 55mm. diam. £648

An 18ct. gold keyless lever watch, signed Dent, the case with thief proof pendant marked London, 1921, 52mm. diam. £2,200

An 18ct. gold keyless lever chronograph, the movement signed Nicole & Capt., London, Patent No. 7255, 48mm. diam. £520

An enamelled gold openface dress watch of Napoleonic interest, signed Movado, the 18ct. gold case with London import mark 1910, 47mm. diam. £1,882

A gold minute repeating lever watch, the ¾-plate movement signed Jos. Penlington, Liverpool, No. 12937, 51mm. diam. £1,620

WATCHES
NAMED

Gold half quarter-repeating duplex watch by Sam Archer, London, 1812, 52mm. diam. £1,080

18ct. yellow gold cased open-faced English lever pocket watch, signed Pegler Brothers, Norwich. £225

Gold and enamel cylinder watch by James McCabe, London, circa 1790, 49mm. diam. £1,500

A Swiss gold and enamel bridge-cock verge watch signed Alliez Bachelard & Terond Fils N. 61141, 45mm. diam. £756

A gold openface free sprung fusee lever watch with winding indicator, signed Aldred & Son, Yarmouth, the 18ct. gold case, London, 1891, 53mm. diam. £806

A gold repousse pair cased verge watch signed Wm. Addis London 1812, 48mm. diam. £1,190

A silver pair cased verge stop watch, the movement with pierced cock signed Thos. Munro, London 1146, 57mm. diam. £340

A gold pair case verge watch set with rubies, signed Jos. Martineau Sen., London, 53mm. diam. £16,170

A gold openface cylinder watch with eccentric dial, signed Jn. Louis More, 45mm. diam. £200

**WATCHES
NAMED**

Gold pair-cased quarter
repeating watch by Tho.
Mudge, London, 53mm.
diam.   £2,250

An 18ct. gold hunter-cased
keyless lever watch, signed
Nicole & Capt., London,
Patent No. 2932, 44mm.
diam.   £320

A silver verge alarm
watch by Charles Oudin,
circa 1820, 57mm. diam.
£385

A French gold, enamel and
pearl verge watch, the bridge-
cock movement signed Martin
A Paris 11750, 37mm. diam.
£1,540

A Dutch enamel and silver
pair cased verge watch with
false pendulum, signed Martineau, London, 52mm.
diam.   £1,024

An 18ct. gold minute repeating keyless lever watch, the
movement signed James
Murray, London, 1882,
51mm. diam.   £950

A Swiss gold and enamel
cylinder watch, the move-
ment signed Mottu, Geneve,
34mm. diam.   £702

A gold openface split second
chronograph, signed C. H.
Meylan, Brassus, 48mm.
diam.   £504

A gold floral enamel dress
watch, signed L. Gallopin &
Co., Suc'rs to Henry Capt,
Geneva, 44mm. diam.
£1,210

**WATCHES
NAMED**

Early 19th century quarter repeating gold pocket watch, by Moulinie Bautte & Moynier, Geneve. **£600**

A gold hunting cased minute-repeating keyless lever watch No. 1720 by S. J. Rood & Co. of London, hallmarked 1889, 53mm. diam. **£1,980**

Silver open-faced full plate keyless tourbillon watch by Mobilis, 53mm. diam. **£1,750**

A gold quarter repeating duplex watch, the movement signed Rd. Webster, Cornhill, London, 5248, 53mm. diam. **£669**

A Swiss gold and enamel open-faced keywind watch, signed Milleret & Tissot a Geneve, 34mm. **£440**

An 18th century verge pocket watch with silver dial and case, by J. Hocker, Reading. **£190**

An 18ct. gold open faced keywind watch, the engraved cock signed Margeret Wilson, hallmarked 1845, 44mm. diam. **£250**

A gold, enamel and split pearl-set verge watch by Thos. Gray of Sackville Street, circa 1780, 47mm. diam. **£3,080**

An open faced keyless cylinder fob watch, the movement stamped Savoye Freres & Cie, signed on the cuvette Faucard a Dinard, 30mm. diam. **£200**

WATCHES NAMED

Fine gold keyless free sprung lever dress watch, signed Jump, London, 53mm. diam.
£1,300

A gold keyless free-sprung lever watch, movement signed Karl Zimmerman, 55mm. diam.
£1,000

A slim gold and champleve enamel cylinder watch by Edward R. Theurer, circa 1850, 45mm. diam.
£1,870

A gold verge watch by Andre Hessen of Paris, 52mm. diam., circa 1790.
£902

A gilt metal and tortoiseshell pair cased quarter repeating verge watch made for the Turkish market, signed Geo. Prior, London, 62mm. diam.
£800

A French gold skeletonised cylinder calendar watch, the dial plate signed Fleury A Nantes, 33mm. diam.
£1,026

An 18ct. gold half-hunter cased quarter repeating pocket watch, inscribed A. Bach, London
£760

Early 19th century Rentzsch duplex movement watch, 96mm. diam.
£715

A gold duplex watch, the movement signed Radford, Leeds, No. 2588, 53mm. diam.
£972

WATCHES
NAMED

A Swiss gold and enamel verge watch, the bridge-cock movement signed Ph^e. Terrot, 57mm. diam. £1,000

Early 18th century silver verge oignon by Etienne Dominice, 58mm. diam. £1,500

A gold open faced lever watch, by G. E. Frodsham, London, hallmarked 1877, 56mm. diam. £600

A gentleman's 18ct. gold half hunter cased keyless pocket watch, inscribed C. R. Pleasance, Sheffield. £160

A Swiss repousse gold quarter repeating bridge-cock verge watch signed Terrot & Thuillier Geneve 5889, 49mm. diam. £1,458

A French quarter repeating cylinder watch, the gold cuvette signed Leroy et fils Horloger Du Roi A Paris No. 4001, 45mm. diam. £864

A French gold and enamel pocket compass sundial, signed Armand a Paris, 50mm. diam. £486

A gold duplex watch, the full plate movement signed John Newton, London, No. 604, 54mm. diam. £540

An 18ct. gold openface quarter-repeating ruby cylinder watch, signed Ph. Fazy, dated 1816, probably Geneva, 52mm. diam. £571

WATCHES NAMED

A small gold half-hunter cased minute repeating free-sprung lever watch, movement signed Joseph Fleming & Co., 40mm. diam.   £2,000

A gold hunter-cased chronometer, the enamel dial signed French, Royal Exchange, London 18567, 51mm. diam.   £972

Swiss gold cased openfaced half-repeating pocket watch, signed Leon Boillat, Geneva   £600

A gold openface minute repeating chronograph with register, signed Touchon & Co., Geneva, 18ct. gold case, 52mm. diam.   £1,366

A nielloed silver sector watch, signed Record Watch Co., Tramelan, 60mm. wide. £921

A gold keyless lever watch, signed Geo. Edward & Sons on ½-plate gilt movement jewelled to the third, 53mm. diam.   £660

A gilt metal and leather covered verge watch, inscribed Quare, London, 2567, 60mm. diam.   £400

A silver pair cased verge watch No. 656 by Andrew Dunlop of London, 56mm. diam., circa 1700.   £1,100

A silver fusee lever watch with winding indicator, signed Smith & Son, London, the case, London, 1899, 52mm. diam. £767

**WATCHES
NAMED**

A gold hunting cased keyless pocket chronometer by J. Bennett, hallmarked 1876, 52mm. diam. £1,320

Silver gilt pair-cased quarter-repeating verge watch by Thomas Grignion, London, mid 18th century, 48mm. diam. £1,000

A gold open face Masonic watch, signed Dudley Watch Co., Lancaster Pa., no. 597. £1,751

A French gold and enamel cylinder watch, the gold cuvette signed J. A. Rossay Palais Royal No 133 Paris, No 2431, 40mm. diam. £702

A platinum dress watch with integral stand, retailed by Bucherer, Lucerne, 42mm. wide. £605

A late 18th century gold and enamel verge watch, the movement signed Gregson A Paris 13123, 50mm. diam. £550

A gold and enamel reversible hunter or openface lever watch, the three-quarter plate movement signed Hamilton & Co., London, No. 35103, 41mm. diam. £734

A gold openface Masonic watch, with nickel 19-jewel movement, signed Dudley Watch Co., Lancaster, Pa., 45mm. diam. £1,008

A small gold openface five-minute repeating watch, signed Fayette S. Giles, 36mm. diam. £1,138

WATCHES
NAMED

A French gold quarter-repeating cylinder watch, gilt cuvette signed Robert O. Courvoisier, 60mm. diam. **£1,750**

A silver-gilt pocket chronometer, movement signed Septimus Miles, plain case, London 1819, 57mm. diam. **£1,240**

A gold and enamel pair-cased verge watch by J. Cowan of Edinburgh, hallmarked 1778 and casemaker's initials IL, 55mm. diam. **£1,850**

A platinum keyless lever dress watch, by Cartier, the signed silver dial with sweep minute hand and with aperture for the hours, 45mm. diam. **£1,400**

A gold pair cased verge watch by Daniel Grignion of London, hallmarked 1726, 54mm. diam. **£1,430**

An 18th century silver and horn pair cased verge watch, signed Conrs. Dunlop, London 3451, the inner case marked London 1762, 52mm. diam. **£1,400**

A slender gold stem wind open faced lever pocket watch, signed Cartier, Paris, 45mm. diam. **£740**

A slim gold and enamel open faced keywind watch with Lepine calibre movement. **£715**

An 18ct. gold open faced keywind watch, signed Cooper, Colchester, hallmarked 1866, 45mm. diam. **£250**

WATCHES
NAMED

Gold free sprung lever
watch, movement sig-
ned Dello Bros. Lon-
don & Bristol, 52mm.
diam.   £900

A chased gold hunter cased
minute repeating lever
watch with automaton,
signed Paul Matthey-Doret,
Locle, 58mm. diam.
                       £5,390

A gold pair cased half
quarter-repeating cylin-
der watch, by John
Cowell, London,
54mm. diam. £1,850

14ct. gold hunting case pocket
watch, 'Elgin', jewelled gilt
movement and white porce-
lain dial.   £250

A 19th century French gold
quarter repeating Jaquemart
automaton watch, 56mm.
diam.   £3,800

A gold openface fusee lever
watch, signed J. R. Arnold,
Chas. Frodsham, London,
1853, 55mm. diam.   £739

Gold pair-cased cylin-
der watch by Alexan-
der Cumming, London,
1781, 53mm. diam.
                   £1,250

A small engraved gold pocket
chronometer, signed Courvoisier
& Comp'e, Chaux-De-Fonds,
46mm. diam.   £403

A gold and enamel verge
watch, Lepine of Paris,
circa 1790, 41mm. diam.
                   £1,320

WATCHES
NAMED

A gold keyless free-sprung
lever Karrusel watch,
movement signed Grant &
Son, plain case, London
1909, 55mm. diam.
£3,565

An enamelled gold pendant
watch and chain, signed Ed.
Koehn, Geneva, retailed by
J. E. Caldwell & Co., Phila.,
29mm. diam.   £672

Gold half hunter cased keyless lever watch by J. W.
Benson, London, 1889,
52mm. diam.   £1,200

A gold pocket chrono-
meter, the fusee movement
signed Wm. Pickman, with
enamel dial and gold hands,
54mm. diam.   £880

A silver pair cased verge stop
watch, the movement with
pierced cock signed Wm.
Graham, London, No. 11437,
the cases marked London, 1797
£210

A French gold and enamel
verge watch, the bridgecock
movement signed Chevalier
et Comp^e 1829, 50mm.
diam.   £810

A gold openface chronograph
with minute recorder mounted
on centre arbour, signed Henry
Capt, Geneva, 55mm. diam.
£638

A gold openface lever watch,
signed L's Audemars, Brassus
& Geneva, 55mm. diam.
£537

A repousse gold pair cased
verge watch by Harry Pot-
ter of London, hallmarked
1780, 53mm. diam. £1,430

WATCHES
NAMED

An American 14ct. vari-
coloured gold box-hinged
hunter-cased watch,
movement signed P. S.
Bartlett, 53mm. diam.
£1,500

A gilt-metal and enamel
verge watch, signed
Cabrier, 50mm. diam.
£600

Gold duplex watch,
movement signed
James Wilson, Lon-
don, 1821, 54mm.
diam. £1,000

A Continental silver pair
cased verge watch, signed
Blanc Pere & Fils, Geneve,
the silver champleve dial
signed P. B., London, 50mm.
diam. £480

A Swiss gold, enamel and
gem set verge watch, the
bridgecock movement signed
Fres. Bordier, Geneve No.
35751, 44mm. diam. £660

A gold pair cased watch, the
full plate movement signed
David Whitelaw, No. 120,
and inscribed Edw Henderson,
Edinburgh 1815, 55mm. diam.
£345

Mid 19th century lady's
18ct. gold open face
pocket watch, Berthoud,
Paris. £490

An 18th century gold pair
cased pocket watch, the
fusee movement inscribed
John Walker, Newcastle upon
Tyne 736. £560

A gold openface medical
chronograph, signed Ulysse
Nardin, Locle & Geneve,
55mm. diam. £1,344

18ct. gold open-faced
key wound lever centre
seconds watch by John
Lecombere, Liverpool,
54mm. diam.   £450

A 14ct. gold case hunter
watch, the movement in-
scribed Invicta Medaille
D'Or 1895, dial 1.7/8in.
diam.   £500

18ct. gold open-faced
keyless lever centre
seconds watch, Ches-
ter, 1880, 53mm.
diam.   £400

An enamelled gilt metal
verge watch, signed Gregson
A Paris, with white enamel
dial, 53mm. diam.   £571

An 18th century silver pair
cased verge watch, signed
G. Bryan, London, 399,
50mm. diam.   £420

A French gold and enamel
verge watch, the bridge-cock
movement signed Hessen a
Paris, 38mm. diam.   £540

A silver repousse pair cased
striking coach clock watch,
signed Johan Georg Brodt,
circa 1725, 126mm. diam.
                   £10,800

A gold and enamel bridge-
cock verge watch signed
Guex A Paris, 52mm. diam.
                   £2,052

A gold and enamel dumb
quarter-repeating verge
watch by Champion of
Paris, hallmarked 1777,
40mm. diam.   £1,760

WATCHES
NAMED

A triple colour gold and
enamel verge watch by
Pierre Bry of Paris,
circa 1790, 46mm. diam.
£1,000

A gold hunter cased quarter
repeating duplex watch,
signed Courvoisier Freres,
18ct. gold case, 50mm.
diam.   £759

A gold and agate verge
watch, movement signed
Hen. Hurt London,
45mm. diam.   £1,750

An enamelled gold cylinder
watch, signed F. Delynne a
Paris, no. 206, 40mm.diam.
£13,475

A gold pair cased verge watch,
signed Jams. Hagger, London
200, 54mm. diam.   £2,530

An openface floral enamel
silver gilt centre seconds
watch for the Chinese Market, signed Bovet, Fleurier,
55mm. diam.   £2,016

An engraved gold openface
lever watch, signed Lucien
Dubois, Locle, 48mm. diam.
£739

A gilt metal pair cased
verge stop watch, signed
James Wild, Soho, 56mm.
diam.   £250

A multi-colour gold filled
hunter cased pocket watch,
signed Illinois Watch Co.,
fifteen jewel movement,
53mm. diam.   £250

WATCHES NAMED

Early 18th century silver verge watch by E. Sherwin of London, 58mm. diam.   £1,250

A gold half hunting cased lever watch by W. G. Hallett of Hastings, hallmarked 1867, 43mm. diam.   £500

William Webster silver pair-cased open-faced verge fusee pocket watch, signed, 1767.   £300

An enamelled gold convertible cased cylinder watch, signed J. FS. Bautte & Co., Geneve, with gilt cylinder movement jewelled to the third wheel, 36mm. diam.   £1,748

A gold Karrusel lever watch, the movement signed John Dyson & Sons Leeds, 55mm. diam.   £3,456

An engraved gold hunter-cased pocket chronometer, signed on the cuvette Constantaras Freres, Constantinople, 55mm. diam.   £806

A Swiss open faced keywind watch, stamped Stauffer, Ce. De-Fond, 38mm. diam. £150

An 18ct. gold hunter-cased keyless chronograph, the movement signed J. W. Benson, No. 2516, London, 54mm. diam.   £1,200

14ct. gold hunting case pocket watch, 'Elgin', lever set jewelled nickel movement and white porcelain dial.   £381

212

WATCHES
NAMED

Cartier platinum and
diamond set keyless
lever watch by the
European Watch Co.,
46mm. £2,250

A gold hunter cased split-
second chronograph with
register, the dial signed
Jules Renaud, 45mm.
diam. £1,010

A gold hunter cased minute
repeating watch, signed L.
C. Grandjean, Locle, 53mm.
diam. £2,021

An 18th century gold and
enamel pair cased watch,
signed Geo. Phi. Strigel,
London, 1770, 48mm.
diam. £1,900

An 18ct. yellow gold hunting cased duplex pocket
watch, by Tolkien &
Gravell, hallmarked London,
1813. £460

A verge watch, quarter-
repeating on two visible bells,
the gilt movement signed
Georg Schmit, Neustadt,
56mm. diam. £1,344

A gold pair case verge watch,
signed Wm. Robertson,
London, 1793, together with
an 18ct. gold chain, 52mm.
diam. £806

An 18ct. gold hunter-cased
minute-repeating chrono-
graph, signed Albert H.
Potter & Co., Geneva,
52mm. diam. £6,387

A Swiss gold and enamel
keyless lever watch, the
dial signed Hartog, 48mm.
diam. £1,296

WATCHES
NAMED

A gold hunter cased minute repeating chronograph with perpetual calendar and moon phases, signed H. Redard & Son, Geneva, 51mm. diam.   £9,432

A silver triple cased verge watch for the Turkish market, the movement signed Isaac Rogers London 18925, 72mm. diam.   £1,404

An 18ct. yellow gold three-quarter plate English keyless lever pocket watch, by Parkinson & Frodsham.   £264

A silver pair cased verge watch with automaton, signed Sylvester, London, no. 6788, 55mm. diam.   £607

A small oval gilt metal verge watch, signed N. Vallin, length including pendant 53mm. £2,970

A French gold and enamel verge watch, signed Dutertre a Paris, 43mm. diam.   £720

An 18ct. gold keyless lever watch, the movement jewelled to the centre and signed S. Smith & Son, the case marked London, 1901, 52mm. diam.   £520

A 9ct. gold Prince Imperial watch, 1932, by Rolex, length overall 41mm.   £880

A cast gold cylinder watch by Rundell, Bridge & Rundell, hallmarked 1817, 44mm. diam.   £1,760

WATCHES
ARNOLD

A silver gilt pocket chronometer by J. R. Arnold, plain case hallmarked 1800, 54mm. diam. **£2,300**

A gold pocket chronometer, the movement signed John Arnold & Son, 53mm. diam. **£5,184**

A silver cased pocket chronometer by John Arnold, London, 50mm. diam. **£8,640**

AUDEMARS PIGUET

Audemars Piguet No. 154003, gold hexagonal cased skeleton keyless lever watch, 50mm. diam. **£1,870**

An openface platinum dress watch with 19-jewel movement with gold train, signed Audemars Piguet & Co., no. 36541, 43mm. diam. **£690**

A skeleton keyless lever watch by Audemars Piguet & Cie, the movement with gold train, 45mm. diam. **£1,650**

BARRAUD & LUNDS

A gold keyless openface free sprung fusee lever watch with winding indicator, signed Barraud & Lunds, London, 1893, 51mm. diam. **£1,142**

A gold hunter-cased lever watch, signed Barraud & Lunds, London, 1882, 50mm. diam. **£470**

A gold open faced lever watch by Barraud & Lunds, hallmarked 1871, 47mm. diam. **£440**

WATCHES
BREGUET

19th century gold and enamel quarter repeating cylinder watch, inscribed Breguet, 47mm. diam.
£2,250

Unusual gold quarter-repeating jump hour cylinder watch, inscribed Breguet no. 2675, 55mm. diam. £1,850

A gold open faced quarter-repeating duplex watch signed Breguet, circa 1840, 45mm. diam. £1,000

A gold jump seconds dual time cylinder watch, gold cuvette signed Breguet a Paris No 4275, 55mm. diam. £2,160

Breguet No. 58: a gold quarter repeating duplex watch, gilt Lepine calibre, 44mm. diam. £2,200

A French gold jump hour cylinder watch with plain balance and gold cuvette inscribed Breguet A Paris No. 8416, 50mm. diam. £1,540

A Swiss gold openface quarter repeating musical watch, signed Breguet, 56mm. diam. £1,821

A French gold and enamel cylinder watch, the movement signed Breguet A Paris, 51mm. diam. £1,620

A gold quarter repeating jump hour ruby cylinder watch, inscribed Breguet No. 2097, 48mm. diam. £3,024

WATCHES
BREGUET

Silver and gold cased watch, signed Breguet, no3233, 62mm. diam.
£7,500

A gold minute repeating keyless lever chronograph, signed Breguet No. 1310, 56mm. diam.
£5,400

Gold cased five minute repeating keyless lever chronograph 'Paris' watch by Breguet, 55mm. diam.
£5,000

A Swiss gold minute repeating grande sonnerie keyless lever clock watch, the cuvette signed for Breguet No. 4722, 57mm. diam.
£23,000

An 18ct. gold openface quarter repeating verge watch with jacquemarts, Swiss, signed on the cuvette Breguet & Fils, no. 23592, 55mm. diam.
£1,842

Early 19th century silver openface clock watch, Swiss, the cuvette signed Breguet & Fils, the top plate signed Japy, 58mm. diam.
£1,008

FRODSHAM

An eight-day fusee keyless pocket chronometer, by Chas Frodsham, hallmarked 1915, 72mm. diam.
£20,900

A gold hunter-cased tourbillon watch, the movement signed Chas. Frodsham, 61mm. diam.
£30,000

An 18ct. gold cased keywind pocket watch by Charles Frodsham, dated 1884, in green morocco case.
£750

WATCHES
JURGENSEN

A gold hunter cased minute repeating watch, signed J. Jurgensen, Copenhagen, 18ct. gold case, 53mm. diam. £4,174

A gold hunter cased lever watch, signed J. Jurgensen, Copenhagen, 18ct. gold case, 50mm. diam. £986

An 18ct. gold openface minute-repeating split-second chronograph with box and certificate, signed Jules Jurgensen, Copenhagen, 55mm. diam. £12,101

LIGHTER

A 9ct. gold combined cigarette lighter and watch by Dunhill, the base stamped Made in Switzerland, 5.3cm. high. £605

A Swiss eight-day silver combined watch and lighter, 1928, 100mm. high. £530

A 14ct. gold combined watch/lighter, the case engine-turned overall, 46mm. high. £550

LONGINES

A gold open faced keyless lever dress watch by Longines, with damascened nickel movement, 44mm. diam. £495

An Art Moderne 18ct. bicolour gold open face pocketwatch, Swiss jewel movement by Longines. £580

An 18ct. chased gold hunter-cased lever watch, signed Longines, with damascened nickel movement jewelled to the third wheel, 52mm. diam. £940

WATCHES
PATEK PHILIPPE

An 18ct. gold openface lever watch, signed Patek Philippe & Cie, Geneve, with nickel movement jewelled to the centre, 50mm. diam. £806

A gold and rock crystal keyless lever dress watch, by Patek Philippe, 46mm. diam. £1,430

A gold openface dress watch, signed Patek Philippe & Co., Geneve, within an 18ct. gold case, signed on movement and case, 48mm. diam. £874

A 14ct. gold openface lever watch, signed Patek Philippe & Co., Geneva, no. 89566, 50mm. diam. £729

An 18ct. gold openface watch minute repeating on three gongs, signed P. Philippe & Co., Geneve, 48mm. diam. £9,108

An 18ct. gold openface dress watch, signed Patek Philippe & Co., Geneva, no. 188192, 42mm. diam. £614

An 18ct. gold openface split-second chronograph, signed Patek Philippe & Cie, 47mm. diam. £2,016

A platinum openface dress watch, signed Patek Philippe & Co., Geneva, with nickel 18-jewel lever movement, 44mm. diam. £1,142

An 18ct. gold openface centre seconds watch, signed Patek Philippe & Co., Geneva, no. 185202, 46mm. diam. £1,535

WATCHES
PATEK PHILIPPE

An 18ct. gold openface dress watch, signed Patek Philippe & Co., Geneve, with nickel 18-jewel cal. 17-170 lever movement, 44mm. diam.
£1,479

A platinum openface dress watch, signed Patek Philippe & Cie, Geneve, on movement and case, 44mm. diam.
£1,075

A large gold openface lever watch, signed Chronometro Gondolo, by Patek Philippe & Cie, 56mm. diam. £1,075

An enamelled platinum openface dress watch, signed Patek Philippe & Co., Geneva, no. 810822, 39mm. diam. £921

An 18ct. gold openface watch with perpetual calendar, signed Patek Philippe & Co., 46mm. diam. £8,740

A two-colour gold openface dress watch, signed Patek Philippe & Co., no. 817759, 45mm. diam. £844

A gold openface lever watch, signed Patek Philippe & Cie, Geneva, retailed by Bailey, Banks & Biddle, Phila., 50mm. diam. £874

A platinum openface dress watch, signed Patek Philippe & Co., Geneva, no. 890237, 43mm. diam. £882

An enamelled gold openface watch, signed P. Philippe & Co., nickel eighteen-jewel cal. 17-170 movement, 44mm. diam. £986

WATCHES
PATEK PHILIPPE

An 18ct. gold openface lever watch, signed Patek Philippe & Co., no. 135231, 45mm. diam. £1,074

An 18ct. gold openface dress watch, signed Patek Philippe & Co., with nickel 18-jewel movement and silvered dial, 45mm. diam. £504

An 18ct. gold openface minute-repeating watch, signed Patek Philippe & Cie, 47mm. diam. £4,370

An 18ct. gold openface chrono-graph, signed Patek Philippe & Co., Geneve, with nickel 23-jewel movement, 48mm. diam. £2,016

A gold openface chronograph with register, signed Patek Philippe & Co., Geneve, 44mm. diam. £3,234

A chased and enamelled platinum openface watch, signed P. Philippe & Co., no. 200063, 43mm. diam. £910

An 18ct. gold openface dress watch, signed Patek Philippe & Co., Geneva, no. 892815, 47mm. diam. £921

A platinum openface dress watch, signed Patek Philippe & Co., Geneva, on movement and case, with original box and guarantee certificate, 44mm. diam. £1,613

A platinum openface split-second chronograph, signed Patek Philippe & Co., 47mm. diam. £3,697

WATCHES
PATEK PHILIPPE

An enamelled platinum open-face dress watch, signed Patek Philippe & Co., Geneva, no. 814228, 42mm. diam.   £844

A gold openface lever watch, signed Patek Philippe & Co., Geneva, on movement and case, 48mm. diam.   £672

A gold openface dress watch with nickel 18-jewel movement, signed Patek Philippe & Cie, 48mm. diam. £1,142

PRIOR

A triple silver and tortoise-shell cased verge watch, by Edward Prior, London, for the Turkish market. £419

A silver triple cased Turkish Market verge watch by E. Prior of London, hallmarked 1882, 65mm. diam.   £660

A quadruple case verge watch for the Turkish market, signed Edw. Prior, London, 70mm. diam.   £4,716

TIFFANY

An 18ct. gold openface five-minute repeating watch, signed P. Philippe & Co., no. 97353, dial signed Tiffany & Co., 45mm. diam.   £2,277

A small 18ct. gold openface five-minute repeating split-second chronograph, signed Tiffany & Co., the movement by P. Philippe, no. 111758, 42mm. diam.   £3,454

A Swiss gold openface split-second chronograph, retailed by Tiffany & Co., N.Y., 18ct. gold case, 51mm. diam.   £1,138

WATCHES
TIFFANY

A gold openface chronograph, Swiss, retailed by Tiffany & Co., New York, signed Tiffany, 53mm. diam. £605

A gold miniature keyless lever watch, the steel bar movement jewelled to the centre and signed for Tiffany & Co., N.Y., 27mm. diam. £340

An 18ct. gold openface minute-repeating split-second chronograph, Swiss, retailed by Tiffany & Co., 54mm. diam. £4,033

TOMPION

A late 17th century silver pair cased verge watch, signed Tho. Tompion, London 0292, 57mm. diam. £1,800

Early 18th century silver pair-cased verge watch by Tompion & Banger, 55mm. diam. £1,750

A silver pair cased verge watch, the movement signed Tho. Tompion, London, 2631, 55mm. diam. £2,808

WALTHAM

An American gold keyless lever watch, movement signed Am. Watch Co., 52mm. diam. £453

A gold box hinge hunter-cased watch, by American Waltham Watch Co., within an engraved 14ct. gold box hinged case, 55mm. diam. £672

A gold openface watch by the American Waltham Watch Co., within a plain 18ct. gold cuvette, 48mm. diam. £806

WATCHES
VACHERON & CONSTANTIN

A gold openface lever watch, signed Vacheron & Constantin, Geneva, within an engine-turned 18ct. gold case, 58mm. diam. **£739**

A finely enamelled gold open-face dress watch, signed Vacheron & Constantin, 47mm. diam. **£2,016**

An 18ct. gold openface lever watch, signed Vacheron & Constantin, Geneva, with nickel bar pattern movement jewelled to the centre, 53mm. diam. **£638**

A 14ct. rose gold openface dress watch and chain, signed Vacheron & Constantin, Geneve, with 17-jewel nickel lever movement, 42mm. diam. **£941**

A gold openface chronograph, signed Vacheron & Constantin, Geneve, with an 18ct. gold fob, 51mm. diam. **£1,210**

An 18ct. gold openface dress watch, with nickel 17-jewel lever movement, signed Vacheron & Constantin, Geneva, no. 486697, 48mm. diam. **£614**

VULLIAMY

A gold openface quarter repeating duplex watch, signed Vulliamy, London, 18ct. gold case, 1835, 45mm. diam. **£986**

A gold hunter-cased cylinder watch, the movement signed Vulliamy, London ruim, 50mm. diam. **£410**

A gold and enamel duplex watch by Vulliamy No. MXRC, signed and numbered on the movement, 41mm. diam. **£1,980**

WRIST WATCHES

A gold wristwatch by Tissot, fitted with a gold Omega strap, circa 1970, 29mm. diam. £300

A Georg Jensen watch designed by Torun Bulow-Hube, round face with no numerals. £1,080

A gold coin watch, 'Le Jour' Swiss movement, in a twenty dollar United States gold piece dated 1904.' £939

An 18ct. white gold and diamond wristwatch by Chopard, 34mm. circa 1970. £1,250

A gold self-winding wristwatch with calendar, signed Universal, Geneva, within an 18ct. gold case. £369

An 18ct. white gold and hardstone skeletonised wristwatch, signed Chopard, Geneve, with original leather strap and 18ct. white gold buckle. £4,370

A gold self-winding wristwatch, signed Piaget, no. 7311215, the leather strap with 18ct. gold buckle. £575

An 18ct. gold wristwatch, signed West End Watch Co., with nickel movement jewelled through the centre. £460

A Swiss 18ct. gold wristwatch with centre seconds, signed International Watch Co., with a 14ct. gold mesh bracelet. £750

WRIST WATCHES

A gentleman's Swiss 18ct. gold cased calendar wrist watch by Leonidas. £460

Hopalong Cassidy wrist watch, complete with original tooled leather band. £100

An 18ct. gold circular wrist-watch, the movement signed European Watch and Clock Co. Inc., the dial inscribed Cartier, 30mm. diam. £620

A Swiss gold wristwatch, gold cuvette inscribed in Russian, the dial signed in Cyrillic Pavel Buhre, 39mm. diam. £1,100

A white gold and diamond wristwatch by The European Watch & Clock Co., 18mm. circa 1925. £2,000

A gold self-winding wrist-watch with calendar, signed Lucien Picard, Seashark, with textured 14ct. gold bracelet. £345

An 18 carat tri-colour gold wrist-watch by Montre Royale, 27mm. wide, London 1976. £1,100

An 18ct. gold wristwatch with 21-jewel movement, signed Corum. £253

A 14ct. gold, ruby and diamond watch, covered Swiss jewelled movement, circa 1940. £1,342

WRIST WATCHES

A gold wristwatch by
Corum, the case and
dial cast as a 1904 $20
gold piece, 35mm., circa
1970.   £1,500

Gold calendar wrist-
watch by Baume &
Mercier, circa 1945,
37mm. diam.   £1,500

Unusual automatic
white gold wristwatch
by Bueche-Girod,
38mm. wide, modern.
                £1,000

A gold wristwatch with nickel
21-jewel movement, signed
Lord Elgin, with 14ct. gold
bracelet.   £291

An 18ct. gold and enamel
wristwatch, 1924, by the
Welsam Watch Co., length
overall 35mm.   £290

A white gold wristwatch,
the lapis lazuli dial signed
Piaget with milled band,
24mm. wide.   £900

A gold wrist chronograph
with register, signed C. H.
Meylan Watch Co., the
silvered dial signed Marcus
& Cie.   £1,750

A lady's Viennese gold
wristwatch with square
face, the bracelet formed
from articulated rectangular
plaques, total length
16.50cm.   £480

A lady's platinum diamond
and seed pearl wristwatch,
signed Verger, Paris.£2,964

WRIST WATCHES

Art Deco gold and enamel watch, frame with four diamonds at each corner. £430

A 14ct. gold snake bracelet watch, 'Blancpain', 91gr. without movement. £1,140

Gold and diamond wrist-watch with Swiss movement, 27mm. diam., circa 1910. £380

A gold wristwatch, signed International Watch Co., Schaffhausen, with leather strap with 14ct. gold buckle and a spare crystal. £1,008

A lady's platinum wristwatch, set with 24 small brilliant-cut diamonds, on black silk cords. £120

A steel duoplan wristwatch, signed Jaeger, with oblong nickel lever movement, the white dial signed Cartier. £1,210

A gent's gold rectangular digital wristwatch, on a gold bracelet. £380

An early self-winding wristwatch, signed Harwood Self Winding Watch Co. Ltd. £125

An American 14ct. gold wristwatch, signed Hamilton, with a 14ct. gold mesh bracelet. £500

WRIST WATCHES
AUDEMARS PIGUET

A platinum wristwatch, signed Audemars Piguet, on the movement and case, inscribed and dated 1926 in the interior. £4,033

An 18ct. gold wristwatch with centre seconds, signed Audemars Piguet, with nickel 20-jewel movement with gold train. £1,479

A gold wristwatch, signed Audemars Piguet, with 18ct. gold bracelet, signed Tiffany & Co. £1,080

A gold wristwatch, signed Audemars Piguet, no. 58098, with nickel 18-jewel movement. £652

BREGUET

A thin gold wristwatch, signed Audemars Piguet, with nickel 20-jewel lever movement. £800

A gold wristwatch within an 18ct. gold case, signed Audemars Piguet, with 14ct. mesh bracelet. £696

A steel wrist chronograph, signed Breguet, and another signed Henry K. Tournheim-Tourneau, without calendar. £1,075

A platinum wristwatch with 17-jewel movement and sapphire crown, signed Breguet, no. 4300. £1,535

A gold wristwatch, signed Breguet, no. 3150, with leather strap and 18ct. gold deployant buckle. £1,535

WRIST WATCHES
CARTIER

A gold wristwatch by Cartier, with a double border enclosing the winder, 27mm. £950

An 18ct. gold wristwatch by Cartier, hallmarked London 1963, 26mm. £2,200

14ct. gold tank-style watch by Cartier, housing a 17J Concord movement. £350

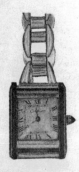

A gold Cartier wristwatch, the movement signed E. W. & Co. Inc., length overall 30mm. £2,750

A Cartier gold wristwatch, rectangular face, hexagonal winder set with a sapphire. £5,940

A Cartier 18ct. gold wristwatch, the movement by the European Watch Co., length overall 26mm. £1,760

A gold and diamond wristwatch by Cartier, the case with diamond set shoulders, 20 x 27mm. £850

An enamelled gold wristwatch, retailed by Cartier, the movement signed European Watch & Clock Co. £6,050

An 18ct. gold wristwatch, retailed by Cartier, the movement signed Jaeger Le Coultre, with oblong duoplan nickel movement. £3,697

WRIST WATCHES
GRUEN

A gold wristwatch with nickel 17-jewel movement, signed Gruen Watch Co., Curvex Precision. £230

A 14ct. gold curvex wristwatch, signed Gruen, with curved cushion shaped 17-jewel movement, £672

A 14ct. gold curvex wristwatch, signed Gruen Watch Co., with curved nickel 17-jewel movement. £1,344

LE COULTRE

An 18ct. gold wristwatch with fifteen jewel movement, signed Le Coultre Co., dated 1934. £1,062

A gentleman's 14ct. gold wristwatch, 'Le Coultre', automatic, Master Mariner, white dial and with a leather band. £100

A gold wristwatch by Jaeger Le Coultre, the dial signed Duoplan, 22mm. wide, circa 1935. £1,650

A gold plated calendar wristwatch by Le Coultre, circa 1940, 34x40mm. £1,000

A white gold mystery wristwatch by Le Coultre, 33mm. diam., circa 1950. £770

A gentleman's 14ct. gold wristwatch, LeCoultre, 17J, complete with a leather strap. £320

WRIST WATCHES
LONGINES

A large silver and stainless steel aviator's hour angle watch, to the designs of Charles A. Lindbergh, by Longines. £4,706

A stainless steel wrist chrono-graph, signed Longines, within a waterproof stainless steel case. £409

A stainless steel chronograph, signed Longines, with lever movement. £134

MOVADO

A gent's Swiss gold wristwatch by Movado, 34mm. diam. £1,200

A gold wristwatch with calendar, signed Movado, within a reeded 14ct. gold case, and a self-winding 14ct. gold wristwatch, signed Bulova. £605

A gold wristwatch, signed Movado, with nickel 17 jewel movement, within a circular 14ct. gold case with unusual lugs. £571

OMEGA

A gold Seamaster wrist-watch by Omega 38mm. circa 1965 £1,250

A gold self-winding wrist-watch with centre seconds, signed Omega Seamaster, the leather strap with 14ct. gold buckle. £201

An 18ct. white gold and diamond wristwatch by Omega retailed by Boucheron, circa 1970, 20mm. £850

WRIST WATCHES
PATEK PHILIPPE

A lady's platinum and diamond wristwatch, signed P. Philippe & Co., Geneve, no. 199809.   £759

An 18ct. thin gold wristwatch, signed Patek Philippe, with nickel 18-jewel cal. 10-200 movement.   £806

An 18ct. gold wristwatch by Patek Philippe, import mark London 1965, 35mm.   £700

An 18ct. gold wristwatch with nickel 18-jewel cal. 23-300 movement, signed Patek Philippe & Co., no. 781179.   £944

A gold wristwatch, signed Patek Philippe & Co., Geneva, no. 794766, with 18-jewel cal. 23-300 movement.   £1,320

An 18ct. gold wristwatch, signed Patek Philippe & Co., retailed by Cartier, with fitted box.   £1,000

An 18ct. gold perpetual calendar wristwatch, 1950/52, by Patek Philippe, no. 967642, 34mm. diam.   £9,900

A gold wristwatch and bracelet, signed P. Philippe & Co., Geneve, no. 851446, 18ct.   £759

A platinum wristwatch, signed Patek Philippe & Co., with nickel 18-jewel movement, signed on movement and case.   £3,025

233

WRIST WATCHES
PATEK PHILIPPE

An 18ct. gold automatic perpetual calendar moonphase wristwatch by P. Philippe, 37mm., with a gold strap.   £7,000

A gold World Time wristwatch, signed Patek Philippe & Co., Geneva, no. 929572, the leather strap with 18ct. gold buckle.   £13,333

A lady's 18ct. yellow gold wristwatch, Patek Philippe, jewelled Swiss movement.   £805

A gold wristwatch chronograph with perpetual calendar and moon phases, signed Patek Philippe & Co., Geneve, circa 1946-50.   £26,950

An 18ct. gold wristwatch, by Patek Philippe, no. 834704, length overall 36mm.   £1,870

A white gold wristwatch, signed Patek Philippe, Geneva, with nickel 18-jewel cal. 23-300 movement.   £1,751

An 18ct. gold wristwatch, signed Patek Philippe & Co., Geneva, no. 743586, with an 18ct. gold mesh bracelet.   £806

An 18ct. gold wristwatch, signed Patek Philippe & Co., with nickel 18-jewel lever movement.   £1,008

An 18ct. gold shaped oblong wristwatch, signed Patek Philippe, signed on movement and case.   £3,025

WRIST WATCHES
PATEK PHILIPPE

A gold centre second wristwatch with perpetual
calendar, signed Patek
Philippe & Co., Geneva,
no. 888001.   £17,333

An 18ct. gold self-winding
wristwatch with perpetual
calendar, signed P. Philippe
& Co., Geneve, no. 1119138.
£6,451

A lady's platinum wrist-
watch, signed P. Philippe &
Co., Geneve.   £476

An 18ct. gold self-winding
wristwatch, signed Patek
Philippe & Co., no. 116018,
with signed 18ct. gold buckle
to leather strap.   £1,074

An 18ct. gold wristwatch,
signed Patek Philippe & Co.,
Geneva, with circular nickel
movement jewelled to the
centre.   £1,882

A gold wrist chronograph,
signed P. Philippe & Co.,
Geneve, no. 868978, nickel
twenty-three jewel cal. 13-
130 movement.   £5,464

A gold chronograph
wristwatch, signed Patek
Philippe & Co., 39mm.
diam.   £2,000

An 18ct. gold wristwatch,
signed P. Philippe & Co.,
Geneve, nickel eighteen-
jewel cal. 9'''-90 movement.
£2,125

A gold wristwatch with nickel
18-jewel cal. 23-300 movement, signed Patek Philippe &
Co., no. 782328, and a 14ct.
gold watch signed Omega.
£1,228

WRIST WATCHES
PATEK PHILIPPE

Gold automatic calendar watch by Patek Philippe, with leather strap, 35mm. diam. £1,500

An 18ct. rose gold world time wristwatch, signed Patek Philippe & Co., Geneva, with nickel movement jewelled through the centre. £21,514

18ct. gold chronograph wristwatch by Patek Philippe, London, 1958, with leather strap. £2,500

An 18ct. gold wristwatch, signed P. Philippe & Co., Geneve, nickel eighteen-jewel movement. £1,062

An 18ct. white gold timezone wristwatch, signed Patek Philippe & Co., Geneva, with nickel 18-jewel cal. 27-HS 400 movement. £5,714

A gold wristwatch, signed P. Philippe & Co., Geneve, nickel eighteen-jewel cal. 23-300PM movement. £1,062

An 18ct. gold wristwatch, signed Patek Philippe & Co., retailed by Cartier. £2,353

An 18ct. thin white gold wristwatch, signed Patek Philippe & Co., the nickel 18-jewel movement with Geneva Observatory seal. £1,210

An 18ct. gold wristwatch by Patek Philippe, in a slim circular case 32mm. circa 1970. £850

WRIST WATCHES
PATEK PHILIPPE

A gentleman's 18ct. gold
wristwatch, Patek Philippe,
Geneva, with white dial.
£738

An 18ct. gold self-winding
wristwatch with perpetual
calendar, signed Patek
Philippe & Co.   £8,404

An 18ct. gold gentleman's
wristwatch, Patek Philippe,
Geneve, 15J.   £967

A gold wristwatch, signed
Patek Philippe & Co., Geneva,
no. 1219325, with 18-jewel
cal. 23-300 PM movement.
£1,100

An 18ct. gold wristwatch
with nickel 18-jewel cal.
27-AM400 movement,
signed Patek Philippe & Co.,
no. 731479.   £767

A gold and stainless steel
wristwatch with calendar,
signed Patek Philippe & Co.,
Geneva, Nautilus model with
reeded black dial.   £2,353

A stainless steel wristwatch,
signed Patek Philippe & Co.,
Geneve, with nickel 18-jewel
movement.   £806

A stainless steel wristwatch,
signed Patek Philippe & Co.,
with shaped oblong 18-jewel
nickel lever movement.
£874

A gold self-winding wristwatch, signed Patek Philippe
& Co., within a signed 18ct.
gold waterproof case.£1,613

WRIST WATCHES
PATEK PHILIPPE

A gold automatic perpetual calendar wristwatch by Patek Philippe. 37mm. circa 1970.   £6,000

A Swiss 18ct. gold wristwatch, signed Patek Philippe and Co., Geneva, signed on movement.
£1,500

A Swiss 18ct. gold case wristwatch, signed Patek Philippe and Co., Geneva.
£850

A gold wristwatch with centre seconds, signed P. Philippe & Co., Geneve, nickel eighteen-jewel cal. 27-SC movement.£1,214

A slim gold wristwatch by Patek Philippe, 33mm. diam., circa 1965.   £880

An 18ct. gold wristwatch, signed P. Philippe & Co., Geneve, nickel eighteen-jewel cal. 23-300 movement.
£1,821

A platinum wristwatch, signed Patek Philippe & Co., Geneva, signed on movement and case.   £4,370

A wristwatch by Patek Philippe, 29mm., circa 1900.   £800

A lady's stainless steel wristwatch with calendar, signed Patek Philippe & Co., Geneva, Nautilus model.   £739

WRIST WATCHES
ROLEX

A gold Oyster wristwatch by Rolex, with self sealing winder, 30mm., circa 1950. £800

A lady's rose gold wristwatch, signed Rolex, gold hands 17-jewel movement with an 18ct. gold bracelet. £660

A two-colour calendar Oyster wristwatch by Rolex, 36mm., circa 1965. £600

A 9 carat gold Oyster wristwatch by Rolex, 35mm. diam., Birmingham 1939. £680

A gold and diamond set Oyster day-date wristwatch by Rolex, 36mm. diam. £3,300

A 14ct. gold self-winding wristwatch with centre seconds, signed Rolex Oyster Perpetual, with a 14ct. gold bracelet. £1,277

A gold self-winding wristwatch with centre seconds, signed Rolex Oyster Perpetual. £1,228

A 9 carat gold Prince wristwatch by Rolex, 20 x 40mm., Glasgow 1930. £1,430

A gold wristwatch by Rolex, the copper dial signed, 36mm. diam., circa 1960. £240

WRIST WATCHES
ROLEX

A gentleman's gold wrist-watch, the movement with 17 rubies, signed Rolex Precision. **£440**

A gold automatic Oyster wristwatch by Rolex, with self sealing winder, 34mm., circa 1955. **£500**

A stainless steel self-winding wristwatch with centre seconds, signed Rolex Oyster Perpetual. **£504**

A two-colour gold wrist-watch with box and certificate, signed Rolex, Prince, no. 77625. **£4,040**

An 18ct. gold self-winding calendar wristwatch with centre seconds, signed Rolex Oyster Perpetual, and a gold filled bracelet. **£1,320**

An 18 carat white and yellow gold Prince wristwatch by Rolex, 25 x 43mm., Glasgow 1929. **£3,300**

An 18 carat gold Oyster day-date wristwatch by Rolex, import mark London 1974, 36mm. diam. **£3,410**

A wristwatch, signed Rolex Prince, the 9ct. gold case bearing Glasgow import mark for 1930. **£2,353**

A gold self-winding wrist-watch with centre seconds, signed Rolex Oyster Perpetual, the leather strap with 14ct. gold buckle. **£1,210**

WRIST WATCHES
ROLEX

An early waterproof wrist-watch, signed Rolex, within a silver case hinged to outer protective silver case. £1,008

A 9ct. two-colour gold Prince wristwatch by Rolex, 25mm., import mark Glasgow 1927. £2,000

A stainless steel and gold self-winding centre seconds wrist-watch with calendar, signed Rolex Oyster Perpetual. £470

A white gold Prince wrist-watch by Rolex with Ultra Prima movement, circa 1930. £1,925

An 18ct. gold self-winding wristwatch with centre seconds, signed Rolex Oyster Perpetual, with gold bracelet. £874

An 18 carat yellow and white gold Prince wristwatch by Rolex, with an Extra Prima movement, 25 x 40mm., import mark Glasgow 1930. £3,520

A stainless steel and gold self-winding wristwatch with centre seconds, signed Rolex Oyster Perpetual. £806

An 18ct. automatic calen-dar gold oyster wristwatch by Rolex, circa 1980. £2,000

A stainless steel self-winding wristwatch with centre seconds, signed Rolex Oyster Perpetual, with steel bracelet. £282

WRIST WATCHES
ROLEX

A stainless steel and gold self-winding wristwatch with centre seconds, signed Rolex Oyster Perpetual.   £322

An 18 carat white gold and diamond wristwatch by Rolex, with a Prima movement, 20 x 45mm., Glasgow 1926.   £748

A gold and stainless steel self-winding wristwatch with centre seconds, signed Rolex Oyster Perpetual, with original guarantee certificate.   £874

A gold Prince wristwatch by Rolex, with an Extra Prima movement, circa 1930, 24 x 45mm.   £1,500

A gold calendar wristwatch by Rolex, circa 1950, 38mm. £4,000

An 18ct. two-colour gold Rolex Prince, 1930, no. 70864, length overall 41mm.   £3,080

A gold self-winding wristwatch with centre seconds, signed Rolex Oyster Perpetual. £690

An 18ct. gold self-winding wristwatch, signed Rolex Oyster Perpetual Day Date, with 18ct. gold bracelet.   £2,016

A stainless steel self-winding wristwatch with centre seconds, signed Rolex Oyster Perpetual, Explorer, with Oyster crown and steel bracelet.-   £282

WRIST WATCHES
ROLEX

A lady's 18ct. gold self-winding wristwatch, signed Rolex Perpetual Super Precision, signed on movement and case. £806

A 14ct. gold gentleman's wristlet watch by Rolex with perpetual chronometer movement. £840

18ct. yellow and white gold Prince wristwatch by Rolex, 43mm. long. £1,500

A stainless steel and gold self-winding wristwatch with centre seconds, signed Rolex Oyster Perpetual, with 14ct. gold and stainless steel bracelet. £1,210

A stainless steel self-winding wristwatch with centre seconds, signed Rolex Oyster Perpetual, Submariner. £470

A gold automatic calendar Oyster wristwatch by Rolex, 35mm. diam., circa 1955. £935

A two-colour Prince wristwatch by Rolex, 20 x 43mm., circa 1930. £1,155

A 14ct. gold self-winding wristwatch with centre seconds, signed Rolex Oyster Perpetual. £476

A 9ct. white and yellow striped gold Rolex Prince, 1931, length overall 41mm. £2,860

WRIST WATCHES
ROLEX

An 18ct. two-colour gold
Prince wristwatch by
Rolex, import mark
Glasgow 1929, 25 x 43mm.
£2,750

A gold automatic Oyster
wristwatch by Rolex,
33mm., circa 1950.
£850

A 9 carat gold Prince wristwatch by Rolex, 20 x 41mm.,
Glasgow 1934. £1,210

TIFFANY

A gold wristwatch by C. H.
Meylan Watch Co., the dial
signed Tiffany & Co., 19 x
35mm., circa 1935. £440

A gold wristwatch, signed
Agassiz Watch Co., dial
signed Tiffany & Co., in
an 18ct. gold case. £1,010

Platinum and diamond
wrist watch by Tiffany
& Co., circa 1925.
£1,000

VACHERON & CONSTANTIN

A Swiss 18ct. gold auto-
matic wristwatch, signed
Vacheron & Constantin,
Geneva. £750

An 18ct. white gold minute
repeating wristwatch, signed
Vacheron & Constantin,
Geneva. £36,977

A thin 18ct. gold wristwatch,
signed Vacheron & Constantin,
with nickel 17-jewel movement,
the leather strap with 18ct.
gold buckle. £874

WRIST WATCHES
VACHERON & CONSTANTIN

A white gold mysterieuse wristwatch by Vacheron & Constantin & Le Coultre, 33mm., circa 1965. £1,000

A gent's gold wristwatch by Vacheron & Constantin, the signed gold dial inscribed Verga, 35mm. diam.   £650

18ct. gold calendar wristwatch by Vacheron & Constantin, London, 1954, 35mm. diam.
£1,300

An 18ct. gold bracelet watch, signed Vacheron & Constantin, on movement, case and bracelet.   £1,479

An 18ct. gold wristwatch, signed Vacheron & Constantin, with nickel 17-jewel P 453/3B movement, signed on movement and case   £1,344

An 18ct. gold wristwatch with nickel 17-jewel movement, signed Vacheron & Constantin, no. 421150.
£1,535

An 18ct. gold skeletonised wristwatch, signed Vacheron & Constantin, with signed 18ct. gold buckle to leather strap.   £3,025

An 18 carat gold wristwatch by Vacheron & Constantin, 25 x 38mm.   £825

A Swiss 18ct. gold wristwatch, signed Vacheron & Constantin, Geneva.
£586

WATCH FOBS

An English gold fob seal with pendant ring and the chalcedony matrix engraved with armorials, 3.2cm., circa 1835.   £150

Late 18th century English gold double-sided swivel fob seal of oval form, 5.3cm.   £450

An early 19th century two-coloured gold fob seal, matrix detached. 2.9cm.   £165

An early 19th century English three-colour gold fob seal, 5.3cm.   £450

Early 19th century Swiss gold musical fob seal with central winder, 4.2cm. high.   £600

An English gold fob seal, 3.2cm., circa 1830. £120

An English gold fob seal, the oval chalcedony matrix engraved with initials MK, 2.7cm., circa 1785. £180

Early 19th century Swiss gold and enamel musical fob seal, 4.2cm.   £810

Early 19th century English gold fob seal with plain oblong bloodstone matrix, 3.8cm.   £380

WATCH FOBS

Mid 18th century English gold fob seal, with pierced scroll handle, 2.7cm. £180

An English gold double-sided swivel fob seal with ribbon-bound reeded pendant, 4.6cm., circa 1790. £285

An English gold fob seal, the oblong carnelian matrix engraved with armorials, 3.6cm., circa 1835. £165

Early 19th century English gold fob seal of large size, oval with reeded and fluted mount, 5cm. £480

A 19th century Swiss gold musical seal with chased foliage handle. £1,100

Mid 18th century English gold fob seal with smoky-quartz matrix, 3.2cm. £330

An English gold fob seal of oblong form, with plain foiled citrine matrix, 4cm., circa 1835. £255

A gold double-sided swivel fob seal with scrolled wire-work mount in the form of two serpents, 5cm., circa 1810. £1,141

An English gold fob seal with armorial-engraved oblong citrine matrix, 4.1cm., circa 1835. £300

WATCH FOBS

Late 18th century gold and citrine fob seal, with reeded handle, 1¼in. £250

Early 19th century large gold fob seal with open back. £1,400

A gold fob seal, the cornelian base inscribed 'Registrar of Colonial Slaves', circa 1820, small chip. £453

Late 18th century gold-mounted hardstone fob seal with handle carved as a spaniel, inscribed 'Liber-tie'. £750

An early 19th century Swiss gold musical fob seal, maker's initials JJ.H. £1,080

A 19th century Swiss gold musical fob seal, 3.5cm. £700

A German fob seal, pro-bably Ludwigsburg, circa 1765, 3.25cm. long. £1,000

A varicoloured gold musical fob seal with commemorative portraits of Napoleon I and Josephine and an erotic automaton, Swiss, early 19th century, 42mm. high. £10,757

A 19th century gold musical fob seal, play-ing an animated tune, 4cm. £650

INDEX